ACPC
NCSS-Polish Perspectives
virginiaegg@cox.net
703-501-6152

The story of bridge engineer Ralph Modjeski

A Man Who Spanned Two Eras

There can be little doubt that in many ways the story of bridge building is the story of civilization. By it we can readily measure an important part of a people's progress.

Franklin Delano Roosevelt

The story of bridge engineer Ralph Modjeski

A Man Who Spanned Two Eras

by

Józef Głomb

translation from the Polish language by

Peter J. Obst

edited by

Halka Chronic

The Philadelphia Chapter of the Kosciuszko Foundation
An American Center for Polish Culture

Translations by Peter J. Obst:

Lech Walesa: Democrat or Dictator, Jaroslaw Kurski (Westview)
My Flights to Feedom, Ludwik B. Domanski (WBT)
A Family from Sosnowiec, Kazimierz Cimoszko (WBT)

"A Man Who Spanned Two Eras" is the English language version of "Człowiek z pogranicza epok" by Józef Głomb as translated by Peter J. Obst and edited by Halka Chronic.

International Standard Book Number (ISBN)   0-917004-25-6

Biography–Ralph Modjeski (Rudolph Modrzejewski)

Cover photograph of the Benjamin Franklin Bridge by Peter J. Obst.

Printed and bound in the United States of America.
Published by The Philadelphia Chapter of the Kosciuszko Foundation 2002.

Dedicated to

Edward Pinkowski

Contents

Illustrations

Foreword

This book, before it found its way to the American reader, had two editions in Poland. Its subject, Rudolf Modrzejewski (Ralph Modjeski) was accurately described by the author as a man who spanned two eras. He was also a man who spanned two worlds, the Old World and the New World. He embodied the best qualities of both eras and of both worlds. He had the unique ability of combining the romantic artistic imagination taken from the Old World, and belonging to the passing era, with the sweep of engineering innovation and technical thought that was at the core of the nascent industrial civilization then developing at an astounding pace in the New World. He was living proof that man's most impressive accomplishments are always "on the boundary line." He was more than an engineer and builder, first of all he was a creative person. Fame and money were less important to him than an accomplishment in which he could take pride.

Ralph Modjeski, when asked by one of the visitors to his New York office about the impressive collection of medals, awards, and certificates hanging on the wall, replied "Oh, I have big ones and little ones. The big ones I got quite by accident, and the little ones were given to me because I already had the big ones."

A commission was organized to investigate the catastrophe at Quebec Bridge and to draw up specifications for a new bridge. Its members were: Canadian engineer H. E. Vantelet, American Ralph Modjeski, and the Englishman Maurice F. Fitzmaurice. Later, when telling the story Ralph Modjeski joked that "The Canadian was actually French, the Englishman — a Scot, and the American — a Pole."

These two short anecdotes, contained in the book, wonderfully illustrate Modjeski's character and show that he had an excellent sense of humor.

Rudolf Modrzejewski always remembered his roots, he was aware that they were the source of his esthetic sensibilities. This marvelous linking of esthetics with precision and boldness in construction is noticeable in all of his works. And it is worth knowing that he had built over 200 kilometers (125 miles) of bridges. It is difficult to say which of these structures is his greatest work, though definitely the Benjamin Franklin Bridge in Philadelphia and the Oakland Bay Bridge in San Francisco are among the most impressive.

The excellent book written by Professor Józef Głomb shows us an outstanding engineer-builder in the context of his times and surroundings. We are able to see him not only as an engineer but as a son, a husband, father, artist, world citizen, and one-man institution. In this book the reader will find photographs of the people who were close to Modrzejewski and of the imposing structures he created. There also is a map of the American continent on which the places where he built bridges are marked. Each structure is a lasting mark made by Rudolf Modrzejewski — the Pole, and at the same time by Ralph Modjeski, the American, who could be both an artist and engineer.

I am happy to know that his story has reached the hands of an American reader.

Przemysław Grudziński
Ambassador of the Republic of Poland
Washington, D.C.
March 15, 2001

Preface

Translation from the Polish language and publication of the book by Józef Głomb is a momentous event in modern Polish-American literature. The author portrays Rudolph Modrzejewski (whose American name was Ralph Modjeski), an outstanding Polish-American civil engineer, across the canvas of the two eras of technology, the past and the contemporary. An era, in time chronology, is an interval in the periodical sequence of events chosen according to dominating characteristics. The book refers to the technological definition of the word "era" as one in which technology is the main determinant; but, history, politics, sociology and economy also contribute foundationally.

Ralph Modjeski lived during a cogent time: the end of the nineteenth and the beginning of the twentieth centuries—a time that heralded the merging of the two most interesting eras in the development of civilization. The older era, which began with the Renaissance and lasted several centuries, was summarized by Immanuel Kant's motto "dare to know." That era spawned many scientific and technological discoveries that made our lives easier and more comfortable. The newer era began with the first results of radiation and atomic research, the theory of relativity, development of computers and methods of communication that broadened our knowledge and called our attention to invisible problems of existence of which our ancestors were previously unaware.

The Renaissance itself flickered into the spotlight with the ingenious art, inventions and engineering projects of Leonardo da Vinci. The rapid development of several scientific theories and works of other Men of the Renaissance soon followed. One of them, Nicolaus Copernicus, in 1530 explained the heliocentric system. Another Man of the Renaissance, Galileo Galilei, made several observations that changed the way of thinking of his contemporaries. Upon entering a church, he noticed a chandelier swinging. Although he was only seventeen years old at the time, it occurred to him to compare the rhythm of his pulse with the rhythm of the swinging chandelier. He noticed that the period of oscillation remained constant even though the amplitude became smaller and smaller. Galileo concluded that the period of oscillation was independent from that of amplitude.[1] Simultaneously dropping two objects of different weights from the leaning tower of Pisa, he also concluded that objects of differing weights fall in the same amount of time when dropped from the same height. Exploring the Copernican theory further, he built a 20X-magnification telescope and discovered two previously unknown moons of Jupiter. Leonardo, Copernicus and Galileo were the harbingers of numerous discoveries and achievements in mathematics, astronomy, physics and other sciences that occurred later, from the fifteenth to the beginning of the twentieth centuries.

Hundreds of major technological inventions were introduced during this period. The discovery of universal gravitation by Isaac Newton in the seventeenth century plus his laws of motion became major theoretical tools for physics and technology. James Watt in 1769 patented the improved steam engine invented in its original form by Thomas Savery. Discoveries of Andre Marie Ampere in 1820 and Michael Faraday in 1831 laid the foundations for the principle of the electric motor. Christian Huggens designed the first internal combustion engine fueled with gunpowder in 1678. Dutch inventor Cornelis Drebbel built the first submarine in 1620, constructing it of wood and covering it with leather. Then 150 years later, the first combat vessel submarine, the famous "Turtle," was built by American engineer David Bushnell, a venture that laid the groundwork for later successes but proved unsuccessful under battle conditions at the time.

In 1850, Elisha Otis demonstrated the first brake which allowed the manufacture of safe elevators. Rudolph Heinrich Hertz in 1886 and Guglielmo Marconi in 1896 laid the foundations for modern radio transmission. In 1840, Humphry Davy used an electric arc to produce light, followed by Thomas Alva Edison's construction of the incandescent electric light bulb in 1879.[2]

In 1877, Alexander Graham Bell produced the first telephone that could transmit and receive the human voice with all of its quality and timbre. Otto Lilienthal flew on batwing gliders in 1894; and the Wright brothers, Wilbur and Orville, made four successful powered flights on December 17, 1903. Gottlieb Daimler patented his first four-cycle, single-cylinder motor in 1887; and, in 1896, Henry Ford caused a sensation on the streets of Detroit with his motor-powered "quadricycle."

By the beginning of the twentieth century, all the technological wonders of the modern world: steam and combustion engines, an electric motor, the electric light, a radio, the telephone, a safe elevator, a car, a glider, an airplane and a submarine were invented. Some of them still required further manufacturing and production refinement to be adapted and used in everyday life, but they were already known.

However, the most impressive works seen by the public were enormous civil engineering structures. A 984-foot (300-meter) tall tower, designed and built by Alexandre Gustave Eiffel, was the world's largest construction. The tower was fashioned of puddle iron with cast iron parts, and especially erected for the Paris Exhibition in 1889. Optimized for equal normal stresses under its own weight, it was a visible tribute to the development of engineering science and practice that had started about five hundred years earlier with the works of Leonardo da Vinci. It was the utmost achievement of the iron building. Though the world was impressed with the Eiffel Tower, a new epoch of

steel, alloys and composites was already underway. In structural engineering, it was marked by the introduction of new materials and by even longer spans of bridges.

The beginning of the twentieth century marked the start of the new era for probably the next few centuries, during which new discoveries immensely influencing human life and knowledge are continuing to be made. The new era was marked by the Firth of Forth Bridge that, unlike the iron Eiffel Tower, was completely made of steel. The bridge was erected in 1882–1890 at Queensferry, Scotland. Shape optimized according to the variation of bending moments, it was designed and built by John Fowler and Benjamin Baker as the first major steel structure of this magnitude. Their contemporaries were impressed and the structure enjoyed wide publicity. No wonder that, in such an atmosphere, the study of science and engineering was becoming more and more popular.

There is no proof that young Ralph Modjeski had read about the plans to design the Firth of Forth Bridge as it was finished five years after he graduated, but it is likely that he had heard of it. Traveling with his mother, he visited Paris and saw the Eiffel Tower. Perhaps the impression of the Eiffel Tower and the fame of new bridges then in design and construction during that time, influenced his decision to become a structural engineer, with bridge building as his specialty.

Bridge structures have a very significant place among building constructions. The design and building of bridges represent enormous challenge and adventure, rewarding the designer with a sense of great satisfaction.

That adventure comes not only from the fulfilling the technological dreams, but also because of the meaning of bridges for mankind. From the beginning of human history, bridges were and are a very substantial element in the development of transportation, civilization and culture of people and societies.

At first, hunting, foraging and farming were the main means of livelihood, but later trading and manufacturing goods pressed man to find ways to bring the traffic across the swamps, rivers, gulfs, valleys and other interfering objects and to transport himself, his possessions and goods for trading.

First, pedestrian bridges, built from vines and

ropes plaited of natural fibers, enabled access to difficult-to-reach places. They were easy to disassemble and install in other places. They were very significant elements of defense and created a feeling of safety for those who were sheltered by them. In times of war, bridges were part of the defense system.

Drawbridges defended castles. Other bridges were necessary for the transportation of military personnel and equipment. They enabled the marches of infantry, cavalry, and artillery and later, motorized divisions; they were and still do represent strategic points, and thus they become objects of the battles and maneuverings of armies.

In ancient times, the art of bridge building was learned by priests; in medieval times, by monks; and during the Renaissance, by masters of carpentry and bricklaying. These masters passed on the knowledge to their sons, generation after generation. Their bridges were built starting with abutments and containing the plans of the bridges drawn on their walls. Construction of bridges continued through many years, through the efforts of many people. Often inhabitants of entire regions, nations and countries were involved in the project. At the earlier stages of bridge building, wooden fibers, strips of leather, timber, clay, stone and even ice and snow were used as building materials. Later, bricks, rough iron, concrete, steel, reinforced concrete, pre-stressed concrete, glue bonding and bolts connected timber, followed by the introduction of composites.

Bridges have played an exceptional role in the history of towns, cities, and states in both their civilization and in their human culture, and also in politics. They drew the attention and care of their users, and particularly the rulers, people of the government and other influential persons.

Rulers of countries, kings, state governments, leaders of societies and religious leaders were interested in the construction of bridges. This was not only to render their grandness memorable, in the same manner as it was when they were building towers and spires, big domes, magnificent tombs and pyramids, but also for practical reasons. They pretended to have knowledge of building bridges and directed their construction. Roman emperors assumed the title of the "greatest bridge builder" (Pontifex Maximus), which was passed to the pope together with the title of bishop of Rome.

There are legends, stories and anecdotes about bridge construction. The ruler of Mesopotamia, Nebuchadnezzar II in the sixth century B.C. changed the stream of the river Euphrates, erected the bridge in the dry bed of the river and then directed the river back under the bridge.[3]

There is also a Silesian story that occurred in the early twelfth century. It seems one of the Silesian princes ordered his subjects to keep bringing eggs to glue the stones of a new bridge under construction. For centuries it has been known that glair made from the white of an egg is one of the strongest glues that can firmly join different materials including stones.

Also the leaders of new movements and revolutions were themselves involved in bridge constructions.

A Polish bridge builder Mieczysław Natorff during one of the seminars of the II (Second) Chair of Bridge Building at the Warsaw University of Technology was lecturing on the building of bridges over the Volga River. It was during the years 1918–1919 just after the revolution in Russia. Natorff wanted to return to Poland; however, the revolutionary government would not allow it because of his knowledge of bridge building and design. Leon Trotsky, who at the time was the leader of the revolution, made that decision.

Trotsky proposed to Natorff a condition which he did not believe the bridge builder could fulfill: to reconstruct one of the most important bridges over the Volga River near Syzran with conditions so strict and timing so stringent that it would be virtually impossible to complete. Natorff, however, undertook the task, risking his life. Trotsky's condition was that if Natorff did not finish the job according to the conditions, he was to be executed. With an enormous effort, he finished the job before the deadline. He was paid in gold rubles and allowed to leave for Poland with his family. Many such stories abound about the adventures and misadventures of bridge builders.

People of great intelligence, personalities, interests and ambitions were fascinated with bridge design and construction. Building a bridge could be the major accomplishment of their lives and often resulted in sickness or even death. Sometimes the continuation of the task was extended to the next generation, as it was in case of John Roebling and his son, Washington.[4]

Construction of long-span bridges has always proved a historical and monumental venture so complicated that even with today's advanced technology, a big economic effort is required from societies and even states.

When Joseph B. Strauss built the Golden Gate Bridge, he spent twenty years convincing people, the government and bankers of the state of California about the necessity of undertaking and financing that tremendous effort.[5]

Parts for long span bridges and especially cables for suspension bridges were and still are manufactured by major industries of countries over a period of several years. Such bridges as Firth of Forth, Golden Gate, Verrazano Narrows, George Washington Bridge, Bosporus and Akashi Kaikyo are milestones in the nations' history of technology, not only for their utility value but also their influence on the landscape and influence on the economy of regions. The concrete-arch bridges designed by Robert Maillard changed the landscapes of the valleys of Switzerland.[6]

Bridge builders and designers were always a very specialized group of engineers. Their profession demands courage, foresight, and persistence. Many times during construction their very lives may be at risk. Bridge design demands a high knowledge of mathematics, physics and engineering science. Possessing that knowledge, at the same time, many bridge engineers were very humanistically inclined and were lovers of philosophy and art. While most of the public tend to view engineers as being completely immersed in their own technical worlds, they would be surprised to discover that many bridge builders and designers blend their technical and humanistic passions in their work and hobbies. Therefore, unknown to most, high technological abilities and great humanistic talents are often personal characteristics of bridge builders. In the process of building bridges, engineers are able to visualize and understand their roles in culture, economics and the life of societies in general. In his activities, Józef Głomb shows such understanding, and his book about Ralph Modjes-

ki reflects this to a superlative degree. He is not only an engineer but also a humanist at the same time.

With Józef Głomb, aside from friendship and common interests, we also share the admiration of several great Polish professors and mentors of bridge building over the past century. Some of these include Zbigniew Wasiutyński, Franciszek Szelągowski and Stefan Kaufman. The first two were leaders of the Chairs of Bridge Building at the Warsaw University of Technology.[7] Stefan Kaufman, a professor at the Silesian University of Technology was often a guest in Warsaw.

The atmosphere among the teaching staff and the students of the Bridge Section of the Warsaw University of Technology (WUT) was different than in other sections. Hence, the studies in the Section were more difficult than in other sections of the Civil Engineering Department. The students of the Bridge Section, among other subjects, had to master theory of structures, design theories and technical and architectural drawings.

Every student had to design five bridges before the topic of his/her diploma work was issued. Difficult lecture material and complicated design projects made studies in that Section very challenging. As a result, usually only a few very dedicated students chose to study bridges. Allow me to share a personal example: in my class of 1956–1958,[8] seven out of approximately 200 students, only about twelve decided to study bridge design.

Each student may have had different motives for such a decision. Among them, however, except for the dreams of designing outstanding structures, very common was the desire to work independently and be the leaders of the project in cooperation with architects.[9]

The lectures, seminars and discussions in the Bridge Section concerned not only bridge design and construction but also included general topics of physics, economy, praxeology and humanities. We closely followed and were all under the influence of new technologies and discoveries and discussed their consequences. We felt the atmosphere of the new epoch that was already upon us. It was the age of atomic energy, computers and space exploration and the age of steel, reinforced and prestressed concrete, composites and other new materials. It was the age of calculations and optimization in engineering.

Among the most important discoveries opening the new epoch were findings on radiation by Pierre and Marie Curie.[10] Max Planck's quantum theory, Albert Einstein's general theory of relativity, Ernest Rutherford's experiments in nuclear physics, Joseph John Thompson's discovery of the electron and James Chadwick's discovery of the neutron. These and several other discoveries (though they were in physics, not in engineering) had a tremendous impact on the way of thinking for people involved in technological fields.[11]

They all marked the new era, in which we now live, and inspired us to the future thinking and predictions. In structural engineering it is marked by new even more courageous designs, taller buildings and longer spans of bridges. All these were topics of almost daily discussions with professors in classes as well as during seminars and meetings.

During those discussions, new ideas in materials, for example: super high-tension steel and alloys, fiberglass reinforced concrete and cementless composite aggregate, new ways of analyzing stresses and deformations as well as the optimization of shapes, and many others were discussed.

I myself was under the influence of the great engineering ideas and humanism of Zbigniew Wasiutyński, and, in my opinion, I believe Józef Głomb was as well. Prof. Józef Głomb was, and still is, a great propagator and developer of the new bridge building ideas started by Z. Wasiutyński, not only in Silesia, but also outside of it. Perhaps because of his Silesian type of last name or perhaps for the other reasons he was and is in great love with the region. It was and it is a warm and passionate love. In all his activities, he is as Silesian as the great Silesians and as Polish as the great Poles in the history of Poland.

I met Józef Głomb at Warsaw University of Technology (WUT) in the hall leading to the offices of the Section of Bridge Building. He was there to meet Zbigniew Wasiutyński. At that time he was a slim, young doctor from the Silesian University of Technology (Politechnika Śląska), who had just handed in his habilitation work on the dynamics of bridges.[12] I had read his work before publication and found it most engaging. The hall of the Bridge Section was an exceptional place. Decorated with

drawings of stone, timber, concrete and steel bridges, it had been designed by the best students of WUT from the beginning of the School's history. Many of those students later became well-known bridge designers, scientists and developers. From this hall, one could enter the offices of Wasiutyński and Szelągowski, the most eminent bridge design professors in Poland at the time just after World War II. These professors had a significant influence on the technology, engineering and our/their students' methods of thinking. Wasiutyński impressed us with his courageous visions of technology, inventive design, humanism and general views, whereas Szelągowski inspired us with his precision, exactness, engineering intuition, exact calculation and drawing skills. He alone designed, performed analysis, dimensioned and completely drafted the plans for a nearly kilometer long bridge over the Vistula River in Warsaw.

In the hall of the Bridge Section, lecturers, assistants, students and engineers from industry gathered, eager to converse with professors, and using the opportunity for chatting and carrying on lively discussions. Among them, were many famous engineers and even professors of other universities. We, as students, assistants and lecturers observed that they were rather hesitant, almost like students and graduate assistants, and patiently waited for the professors to finish their previous meetings to see them. In addition to Józef Głomb, in this hall I met for the first time Juliusz Szczygieł, Jan Kimita, Zygmunt Wrześniowski, Andrzej Ryżyński, Maksimilian Wolf and several other engineers and scientists.

When I first met Józef Głomb, I never suspected at that time that this encounter would be the beginning of many years of friendship based on similar views and very close approaches to the science of bridge building and engineering design. It was also my privilege to meet Józef Głomb later on under differing situations. He was always exact in presenting the facts and courageously seeking and defending the scientific and engineering truth. At one time we were both working on the same team of design review of the Katowice Dome, on the Committee of Science of the Association of Civil Engineers and the Committee for Civil Engineering of the Polish Academy of Science. We would see each other during meetings of the Association of

Bridge Builders, called by us the "association of souls." The "members" did not have any identification cards, nor did they pay any dues and everyone who felt that "the goals of the Association were close to him/her" could consider himself/herself to be a member. During those times in Poland, forming new associations, not initiated by authorities, was difficult. Creating the Association of Bridge Builders, with no application and membership based only on the basis of a person's feelings, was the ingenious idea of Zbigniew Wasiutyński.

Józef Głomb often came to Warsaw and attended some of the meetings of the Association. However, he was mainly active in Silesia. He actually was spreading the tradition of combining humanism and technology from Warsaw to Silesia, adding his own original ideas. He was organizing meetings, discussions, participation in bridge design contests, seminars and so called "discussion meetings" in the forest castle in the Silesian National Park. The discussions were devoted to bridge building topics that concerned the role of technology in society and serviceability of technology for humans. After the day of discussion, a nice dinner was held during which presentations about the history of Silesia were given. Dancing followed. Since we attended those meetings with our wives, this ameliorated our home situations. Many of us suffered blame from our families for spending too much time away from home.

Józef Głomb, as a Professor and Head of the Chair of Bridge Building of the Silesian University of Technology, initiated many activities that strengthened positions of Silesian bridge design and construction companies. Participation, together with the Chair led by J. Głomb in the international bridge design competitions for new bridges in Poland and other countries in Europe, resulted in the raising of a company's prestige and business standings.

In his activities, Józef Głomb bonds technology and humanism, and bridge building with the history of nations, their culture and art. By expression of his views and by his works, adding general human values to engineering, he has led us into a world much broader, than the world of technology. Such values allow engineers to see even more clearly that technology is a part of the general human development and civilization. They allow the public to see that it serves the people and contains human values as well. His teachings also permit others to understand how these values initiate bloodless revolutions that are not only expected, but also enthusiastically accepted by everyone, without reservations, because they contribute the good of humanity.

The book about Ralph Modjeski (Rudolph Modrzejewski) is in fact such a contribution. It has technological and cultural meaning, both in American and Polish literature. It shows the contribution of Polish immigration not only into the history of the United States, where Tadeusz Kościuszko and Kazimierz Pułaski are generally known as historical figures, but it also refers to American Technology where Rudolph Modrzejewski (Ralph Modjeski) and Włodzimierz Sendzimir are less known as Polish contributors.

During J. Głomb's visits to the United States we met many times discussing those issues. Most of his time during those visits, Józef Głomb spent in libraries, bookstores, with antique booksellers and in discussions with American, and Polish-American engineers and scientists. Those discussions were about the progress of technology and about the people that were developing the newest technological achievements. They were also about the role of technology and its significant influence on the development of humanity, human culture, civilization, and economy. In those discussions, two general views were present: the analysis of history and experience of the past and the vision of the future coupled with the challenges of the coming times.[13]

In his book Józef Głomb describes Ralph Modjeski's life, his courage, skills, wisdom and hard work with poetical presentation and romanticism, all attributes of pioneers on the frontier of progress.

The book pictures the atmosphere of the changing of times, traditions, customs and technology. At the same time, the book illustrates periods that straddle two eras, the passing and the coming, showing the sequence of events, the events that interlaced through Modjeski's life and that he personally experienced. In 1929, he supervised the building of the Ambassador Bridge a few hundred yards from Beagly Street in Detroit where Henry Ford built his first car, one of the wonders of the passing era. In 1922, he received a Franklin medal together with Joseph John Thompson, whose research was essential to the foundation of atomic knowledge of the new era.

Except for the technology, it is a book about the love of the "old country," causes of emigration, Polish ambition and passion for excellence.

It is a book about the culture and civilization of Poland, the tragedy of the partition of Poland, the darkness of living under Russian, Austrian and Prussian regimes and about the causes of emigration of the people engaged in Polish cultural and political movements. It is a book about outstanding Poles who, after coming to the United States, fell in love with this country and offered their skills and talents to its service. These Poles could be leaders anywhere, but they have chosen this country, America, sharing their contributions to the culture and technology of the United States and of the world.

Readers in the United States and everywhere in the world where English is spoken and understood can read this book to their greater benefit. It would be particularly interesting to those whose family roots, cultural and language traditions are connected somehow with over a thousand years of Polish history.

It would be engaging to those who are watching the course of technological development, and to those who, upon seeing the Benjamin Franklin or Oakland bridges, feel the admiration for the generations of people that created such magnificent breakthroughs in inventive technology. This is the technology that allows us to change the environment, and the technology that causes deep, breathtaking reflections about the unlimited possibilities of human genius.

Zbigniew Marian Bzymek
University of Connecticut
Storrs, Connecticut, June 28, 2002

While writing this Preface, I have received materials, remarks, words of encouragement and help from several colleagues and friends in the United States and in Poland. Especially helpful were remarks of Józef Głomb, Andrzej Marek Brandt and Wojciech Radomski from Poland as well as Harold Brody, Lee Langston, Roman Solecki and Diane Theriaque from the University of Connecticut, and Peter Obst from Philadelphia. I am very grateful for their inputs. I would also like to thank Linda Forman of El Paso, Texas, for the language corrections and reference checks. I owe deep gratitude to my daughters Małgosia and Dorota Bzymek as well as to my wife Danuta Jaworska-Bzymek for reading the first draft of this text and suggesting improvements.

Introduction

Deep in the St. Lawrence River near Quebec, 60 meters below the surface, lie many tons of destroyed steel construction: evidence of a great tragedy — the greatest bridge disaster in the history of bridge building.

Over the river — near this very spot —stands a monumental structure: Quebec Bridge, the longest bridge of its type in the world.

Two human stories are bound up with those two massive collections of steel beams. One tells of how too little was done too late in the face of impending crisis; the other of inventiveness and precision that overcame a formidable obstacle.

The building of a large bridge, never an easy task, often involves many years of struggle with nature. In the endeavor there is not always a clear victor. At Quebec there were both victor and vanquished. Theodore Cooper, the engineer, was among the vanquished. He lost a hard-won reputation and, eventually, like the workers who died quickly in the wreck of his ill-fated bridge, his life. So was not the victor the one who, starting with a total wreck, succeeded in bridging Canada's broad river?

There are great books about great battles and generals. Yet no battle requires the commander to invest several years of unceasing labor, and in no battle does a commander —despite appearances — have to show so much courage and perseverance.

The story of the victor at Quebec, the engineer who came to command there, is the story of Ralph Modjeski, an extraordinary man, a builder of many bridges; it is also the story of an immigrant, one of many, whose life was complicated and adventuresome.

In his youth he was a polite, well behaved boy, a model child, solid as a granite block in the foundation of a large building. Thanks to personal talents and industriousness he managed to step out of his mother's shadow and build his own famous career.

He was a man of his time. His life was unusual because the times in which he lived were unusual. He grew up in a poor country then occupied and ruled by three other nations. There was no way in his homeland to "move up" in society. In such circumstances the adventurous sought places on earth where they could attain their potential. In the nineteenth century the United States was that land of opportunity, while engineering was a sure way of liberating oneself.

He crossed the ocean as a teenage boy and quickly developed roots in his new homeland. He was not an exception for fate drove many from Poland to establish new homes in America where their Polish identities melded with the polyglot population. Americanization of the Modjeski family took its course just as it did in a million families of Polish immigrants, yet never with total loss of sentiment for Poland.

In America Ralph Modjeski reached for the top. Each bridge that he built was another step upward. In his lifetime he built forty large bridges, crossing the mightiest rivers of the continent. In his field he had reached the summit.

But that is not why this book was written. It is important to show not just his engineering achievements but the human side of Modjeski.

Here is a book about a lucky man who found himself in the right place at the right time and was bright enough to seize the moment. The world had to run to catch up with him and with his ideas.

Here's a book about the building of bridges — the story of a man's life who fought against two things — barriers created by nature and the limits of knowledge at the time.

Ralph Modjeski (Rudolph Modrzejewski) at approximately age 70. Photograph courtesy of Modjeski and Masters, Inc.

Chapter 1

Mother and Son

Even using today's criteria, it can be said that Ralph grew up in an unconventional household. His mother, Helena Jadwiga Opid, was born five years after the death of her mother's husband, the Kraków merchant Szymon Benda. She may have been the daughter of Michal Opid, then the family's guardian, whose surname she and her younger sister used until their marriages. Or her father might have been Prince Władysław Sanguszko, a visitor to her mother's home, whose daughter she was said to resemble.

Benda had been a leading citizen in Kraków. During the Napoleonic era he served as a lieutenant in the national guard. In the 1820s he joined the committee for raising Kościuszko's mound.[1] He was a stable citizen with wide interests and some wealth, widely known and respected. The Benda family was probably one of the leading bourgeois families in Kraków.

As a city guardsman, he no doubt tried to cultivate good family values that would indicate respectability, but what could be expected in a situation where there was a thirty-year difference in the ages of husband and wife? He died in 1835. In those times it was difficult for a young widow to support and raise children without male help. However, Helena's early youth passed under good material conditions in a sumptuous house on Grodzka Street, with three older and a younger sister, Józefa. Opid's young son Adolf may have lived with them after his parents' death. Her mother could afford to send her, and her younger sister Józefa, to a private school operated by Salomea Radwańska. But the great Kraków fire (July 18–28, 1850), which destroyed their home on Grodzka Street and another also owned by their mother, ended the financial independence of the family.

The family situation at this time was such that Helena was in constant contact with theatrical life and even took tentative steps to become a part of that world. Her older half-brothers, Józef, Szymon, and Felix Benda were helpful, since they too were taking early steps in theatrical careers. On one autumn evening in 1850 Józef brought home Gustav Zimajer,[2] who quickly became a frequent visitor, friend, and sometime tutor of the family. Helena would later write that he was thirty years old at the time, but apparently he was only twenty-five. The nine-year old girl was absolutely charmed by him.

Ten years later, in 1860, the nineteen-year old Helena and the thirty-five year old Zimajer were living together in Bochnia. With them was Helena's mother, Józefa Benda, and her niece, Stasia. Rudolph, the son of Helena and Gustav, was born on January 27, 1861.

The reasons for moving out of Kraków are not known. There may have been some family in Bochnia, as Józefa's grandfather was said to have been a director of mines there.

Helena made her first stage appearance in Bochnia in June or July of 1861, a few months after giving birth to her son. The income from the amateur performance in which she appeared under the stage name Modrzejewska[3] was distributed among the families of miners killed in a salt mine disaster.

The next two years were especially difficult for Helena as she was beginning her acting career. The travelling troupe, organized by photographer and dance teacher Konstanty Łobojko and imaginatively named the Nowosądecki Society of National Stage Artists gave only a few performances in each Galicia town because of the limited audience. The constant travel, performances in damp, often

Gustav Zimayer (Sinnmeyer) Rudolph's father.

unheated halls, low pay, and frequent hunger, all took their toll.

It was no better during the few months she spent at a theater in Lwów. Finally, in Czerniowiec, the capital of Bukowina, which had just become a part of the Austro-Hungarian Empire, conditions improved: Zimajer became the director of a local theater and probably rose in both social status and income. (Czerniowiec had 30 thousand inhabitants and three theatres—Polish, German, and Rumanian.) Yet, life could not have been easy considering that Helena was working on improving her theatrical technique, which involved frequent changes in repertoire. In addition, in April 1862, between performances in Sambor, she gave birth to her daughter Marylka. A letter written by Helena from Lwów to her mother in November 1862 reveals despite its calm tone the difficult conditions under which she was raising the not quite two-year-old Rudolph and his six-month-old sister. The occasional assistance rendered in those circumstances by Helena's mother was literally worth its weight in gold.

All available documents indicate that Helena wanted to be a good mother, and thought herself as such. But under the existing conditions this was not really possible.

Rudolph's father was a man of small ambitions, not choosy about the methods he used in making money and carving out a career. He had been a low-ranking officer in the Austrian Army, not an outstanding actor, but showed some flair as a theatrical administrator. At first, Helena loved him without limits; later she became aware of his shortcomings and began to look more critically at their relationship. For an ingenue in a touring troupe, he was an important source of support, but to an accomplished actress, recognized in Czerniowiec, one aware of own her beauty and possibilities, he became an impediment.

In the spring of 1865 Helena's little daughter died. In August of the same year, without alerting anyone, Helena left Czerniowiec with the help of her half-brother Felix Benda. She took Rudolph with her, and to avoid arousing suspicions, only the clothes on her back.

Her escape might have been facilitated by Baron Mustazza, a wealthy nobleman living in the border regions, who was also Helena's ardent admirer. All reports from those times praise Mustazza, and there are reasons to believe that the young actress could count on his kindness and support.

Helena returned to Kraków where Felix helped her find employment at a theater near Szczepański Square. Thus began another phase of her life, and from the perspective of time we can see how drastically it differs from that which had gone before. Where possible, Helena tried scrupulously to erase the history of the years that had preceded her rise to fame.

The stay in Kraków started with a battle over the five-year-old boy. Zimajer tried various ways, including the courts, to bring Helena and her son back to Czerniowiec, but he did not succeed. She had too many influential friends and they extended their protection over her. The new director of the Kraków theater, Count Adam Skorupka, obtained police protection for Helena and Rudolph, so, at least for the time being, Zimajer was stymied in his activities.

Helena remained in Kraków for nearly four years, counting a two-month period when she was invited to perform in Warsaw. This period was undoubtedly good for Rudolph as he could make

Helena Modjeska (Modrzejewska) in a photograph from 1895. Photograph courtesy of Jan Zaleski.

Young Rudolph with his father, Gustav Zimayer.

up the nomadic way of life that his parents' profession had demanded. Under the strict, nearly monastic regime that Helena adopted shortly after her arrival in Kraków, Rudolph became the most important person in her life. The time she spent with this intelligent, quickly developing child, bursting with energy, brought her moments of joy that eased the stress of theatrical life.

This was not to last, as trouble was just around the corner. One day in 1866, on returning to her dressing room, she did not find Rudolph there, waiting for her in his usual fashion. He had been kidnapped by his father and taken to an unknown location. At the time, it was said that Zimajer took him to Hungary.

Only after several years of negotiations by Machalski, the best lawyer in Kraków (and a Modrzejewska admirer), was it possible to ransom the child. Helena paid an enormous sum —4,000 gulden. [4]

In the agreement that was then signed, Zimajer also agreed not to use the stage name of Modrze-

jewski. Rudolph was returned to his mother in July 1870.

The sum was large but Helena was at the time the leading actress of the Kraków theater and drew a substantial salary. Still, she had to work very hard. Since the audience in Kraków was small, frequent changes in the repertoire were a necessity. In a four-year period (1865–1869), she played over 100 different roles.

On September 12, 1868, at the Church of St. Anne in Kraków she married Karol Bozenta Chłapowski, a wealthy nobleman-landowner from western Poland. After that, her star continued to rise. Her performances at the Imperial Theater in Warsaw were well received, and she was welcomed at artistic salons held by Maria Kalergis-Muchanov, the daughter of a General in the Russian Tsar's Army. All this took time so Rudolph's upbringing was left to the care of others. The work at the theater in Warsaw was easier than in Kraków, the pay was high, and there were fewer new roles to prepare, but social life took up the lion's share of the Chłapowskis' time. Universally admired and invited to the best salons, Helena enjoyed being in the limelight. But it is difficult to judge today whether the doors to a greater world were opening before Helena Modrzejewska, the actress, or before Mme. Karol Chłapowska, the wife of a prominent nobleman. One thing, however, is certain: a well born husband was a definite asset to her career.

There are facts to back this up; meaningful because she came from Kraków, a region socially "more difficult" than Warsaw. Some time before their departure for Warsaw the Chłapowskis were invited to an audience at the Palace Under the Rams, on the corner of St. Anne Street and the Rynek or Market Place, where resided the noble and extremely influential Potocki family. This invitation indicated that she had been accepted into the highest levels of Kraków society. Errors and sins of the past were forgotten—she was now Mme. Karol Chłapowska. She started her own salon, which attracted the cream of society and the arts. In this setting she shone as the brightest of stars. Reports of her new position in Kraków must have reached Warsaw and probably did much to help open many theretofore locked doors.

In 1869, only six years after the disastrous January Insurrection [5] in Russian occupied Poland, the political situation was still difficult. However, the theater, a bastion of culture, still remained in Polish hands. In addition, protection was extended by His Excellency Sergeij Sergejevicz Muchanov, the former chief of the Warsaw militia, and his wife Countess Maria Kalergis Muchanov, daughter of the Russian General Nesselrode.

We know that Countess Maria, promoted artists in Paris and in the whole of Europe before settling in Warsaw. A beauty herself, she was favorably disposed toward Helena and aided her career. They came from different spheres of life but both must have shared a certain curiosity about life and possibly, though played out at different social levels, had similar experiences during their younger years.

On the other hand, conversations between these people who had just recently been on the opposite sides of the barricade must have been somewhat fragile. Chłapowski had been a soldier of the Insurrection, while Muchanov was adjutant to Great Prince Konstanty. But since a thread of friendship linked the women, political differences between the husbands faded into the background. The historical truth is unequivocal: Chłapowski passed through this difficult ordeal with honor and, never crossed the delicate borderline that separated pragmatic compromise from a betrayal of the national conscience.

During the seven years (1869–1876) that Helena spent in the Warsaw theater, Rudolph remained in Kraków under the care of his grandmother. Like Felix Benda before him, he probably attended St. Anne's Lycee. Only in Galicia, under Austrian rule, could he study in the Polish language. Liberal conditions possible there even allowed the teaching of Polish history. In Russified Warsaw, such studies were out of the question.

The separation did not loosen the ties between mother and son. He would visit her often in Warsaw, and, during summer vacations, they went together to Krynica or, more often, to Zakopane, a mountain town south of Kraków. In a letter from 1872 Helena Modrzejewska wrote that she would spend time by herself, not being sufficiently strong to accompany her husband and son on trips into the Tatra mountains where they "slept in tents or barns." The young boy also participated in sports. In the summer of the following year, Helena took him to Vienna for the Universal Exhibition, and then to Berlin, finishing up with a month in Switzerland.

These were idyllic travels within a liberal, stabilized Europe. There were few border restrictions and passport regulations were minimal. For people with social position and money, the world was an open highway.

The fourteen-year-old boy was the apple of his mother's eye. In her book *Memories and Impressions*, published in 1910, Helena wrote, "Even when he was a boy I was proud of him and had a lot of trust in his common sense, and all that he wished I took to be reasonable…" In a letter from 1875 to her half-brother Szymon Benda she wrote,

> He is now taking piano lessons from Mr. Hoffman, and during seven lessons he learned four of Kohler's etudes and nearly all of Mozart's sixth sonata. In addition, he is studying stenography and languages, and is exercising and riding horseback. Even though he has all these additional activities outside school, he is always first in class and passes for a very strong mathematician…

In a letter to pianist and composer Józef Nikorowicz in Lwów, she mentioned that Rudolph was "in Kraków, studying, and is as wise as a rabbi; or at least his grandmother thinks so…"

There is no doubt that Rudolph was a very able student. The events of his later life show that his mother's opinions were not overstated. Yet, in these expressions, one can see a certain unnatural exultation, no doubt due to the lack of daily contact of the mother with her only son. This psychological alignment is repeated again and again in her domineering behavior toward him and in attempts to intervene in some decisions that later affected his life.

In December of 1875, at the Chłapowskis' Warsaw apartment at 14 Graniczna Street (near the Saxony Gardens), the idea of moving to America was born. The originator of this scheme, which consisted of forming a group that, following in the footsteps of Nathaniel Hawthorne, would establish a communal farm, may have been Henryk Sienkiewicz, then a thirty-year-old author, an admirer of Helena, and a frequent visitor in her home.[6]

However, in her *Memories and Impressions*, she states that the idea of the trip to America came from Ralph who was then visiting her in Warsaw during his Christmas vacation. Already he wanted to be an engineer and builder.

> The first thing that he mentioned in conversation was the coming [Centennial] exposition in

America;[7] looking at a map the boy announced that he would one day build a canal across the isthmus of Panama. He also said that it would be wonderful if we could go to America and see the great celebration, then cross Panama on the way to California. The expression on his face, as he planned the trip, was so joyous that my husband and I started to consider this matter of crossing the ocean as a thing that was quite possible.

But it was probably neither the enthusiastic ideas of the young Rudolph, nor the idealistic and already century-old concepts propagated by Fourier's followers,[8] that influenced the final decision.

Helena Modrzejewska always had an inclination to travel, to lead a nomadic life, and once the decision was made, it was not necessary to wait long for its realization, especially in this group of people used to and experienced in travel. On February 19, 1876, Sienkiewicz left Warsaw for London, continuing to California through New York to pave the way and prepare a place for the group of enthusiasts. On June 21 Modrzejewska give a farewell performance at the Summer Theatre in Warsaw. On the following day she left for a last engagement in Lwów. On July 13 she boarded the ship *Donau* in Bremen and after 10 days arrived in New York. With her were Chłapowski, Rudolph, her maid Anusia, and also Juliusz Sypniewski, who had been imprisoned with Chłapowski in Moabit, his wife and children, and Lucian Paprocki, an artist. Though initially enthusiastic, most of the others who had been guests at the apartment on Graniczna Street decided to pass up the adventure. Among them were Stanisław Witkiewicz (father of Witkacy, an artist), Adam Chmielowski (known as "brother Albert"), and Ignacy Maciejowski.

The move across the Atlantic closed a chapter in the life of this family. For the thirty-six-year-old Helena Modrzejewska, it meant that the center of gravity for her acting career moved to the Western hemisphere. In the next thirty years, she made the ocean crossing fifteen more times appearing in Polish cities in all three zones of partition and gracing the stages of many other European cities. There would be years (1880 and 1881) which she spent entirely in Europe. But from this moment her further career development took place in countries where the English language was spoken.

The trip would have an even greater effect on the life of fifteen-year-old Rudolph. His mother had left behind half of her entire life; he left only his childhood.

Chapter 2

The Great Adventure

Helena Modrzejewska was an exceptional woman. No doubt that talent and beauty were a factor, but moreover she was also gifted with outstanding personal characteristics: multifaceted interests, industriousness, dynamism in all activities undertaken, and a drive toward accomplishment of chosen goals. In every stage of her life she was drawn toward all things that were new. She moved easily from place to place, establishing new contacts, and entering into new communities.

Rudolph inherited all these characteristics, and they were most helpful in his career. He had one additional characteristic: courage. Without it he could not have become a builder of bridges. Such courage was indispensable in that profession, as shown in a statement by the famous American construction engineer David Baerman Steinman. He had calculated that in the United States during the years 1870 to 1880, the period when Rudolph was preparing himself for his profession, an average of 40 railroad bridges had collapsed each year.

Their stay in New York lasted several weeks, enabling the Chłapowski family to visit the Centennial Exposition in Philadelphia, where Rudolph with fascination toured exhibits of machines and equipment. The exposition may have had an influence on the fifteen-year-old, instilling in him a characteristic that would later manifest itself in his designs, a discipline of form, simplicity and purposefulness.

Displays at the Philadelphia exposition, though technical in nature, were understandable to onlookers and conveyed a simple message: function need not by hidden by superfluous detail or ornament of outdated tradition.

The exhibits also revealed the true difference between engineering techniques in America and those in Europe. In nineteenth century Europe there were many trained workers, yet raw materials were not as plentiful. America had raw materials, but, for such a large land, relatively few skilled workers. This dissimilarity created an incentive for mechanization to be introduced more rapidly and effectively into American industry. Soon machines would take over the work of human hands in many fields. Direct contact with technical realities of the New World must have been interesting to the entire group, but in particular to the aspiring engineer.

The busy group of travelers also found time for a trip to Niagara Falls. There, they must have noticed a great bridge finished just three years earlier by another Polish builder, Kazimierz Gzowski. In addition there were other large bridges, such as the unusual 861 foot long suspension railroad bridge built over the Falls by John Roebling thirty years earlier.

New York did not create a good impression on the travelers. Helena wrote that it was a "dirty city without any charm." The group lodged on the east side of the Hudson in Hoboken and had to make their way daily through the dock areas of New York. For individuals acquainted with the cleanliness and order of Switzerland, the differences must have been glaring!

The "colonists" reached San Francisco around September 22, 1876, having crossed the isthmus of Panama by rail (work on the canal would not start for another few years) inspecting the tropical vegetation with great interest. Helena wrote of the trip and the tropical vegetation in a letter to her mother. Their trip from Panama on the liner *Constitution* lasted eighteen days, and was more comfortable than the New York-Colon leg of the journey. After three weeks in San Francisco they proceeded to Los Angeles, where Sienkiewicz was waiting with a carriage that would take them to Anaheim.

The entire journey delighted Rudolph. The enormous difference in distance and living conditions must have been a great attraction to the growing boy. He did not shirk physical labor, but as his mother wrote in *Memories and Impressions* enthusiastically joined (and outlasted) the others in planting and tending orange trees. In the evening he often sat at the piano to play Chopin's waltzes to "convince himself that his fingers have not stiffened up from work."

The beginning of the stay and work on the farm near Anaheim might have been pleasant for all concerned but, largely because of the social composition of the group, it was not successful. The confrontation between dream and reality was too severe.

Sienkiewicz had written that the Anaheim area was paradise. It might very well have been. The group, however, was more accustomed to salon parties than to working in the field, and enthusiasm quickly dissipated. Those who persevered the longest—several months—were Chłapowski, Sypniewski and Rudolph. Chłapowski, having purchased the farm, was attached to the place and he truly liked working the land. The others thought about getting back to city life as quickly as possible.

The material situation did not take long to make its impact. Chłapowski's small fortune and Helena's earnings from performances in Warsaw were melting away like snow on a sunny day. Meanwhile, the farm was not yielding any profits. On January 8, 1877, Helena was in San Francisco, taken there by her husband, studying English and preparing for a return to the stage. Shortly thereafter Sienkiewicz joined her there. He helped Helena with her English, and worked to finish his *Charcoal Sketches*, written under the pseudonym "Litwos."

It was not just material considerations that influenced Helena to leave Anaheim. Helena Modrzejewska did not come to the United States to be a farm housewife. She was too ambitious and dreamed about gaining fame in America, and from America going on to the London stage.

Chłapowski returned to Anaheim. He worked the farm, but at the same time tried to sell it at a good price. Rudolph accompanied him and took an active part in the endless chores. In a letter to his family in Poland, Chłapowski praises him as the most practical individual in the group. "We have

had a great benefit from Rudolph, who is developing both his heart and brain, and one holds great hope that in adulthood he will be a most uncommon man."

Despite difficulties and occasional misunderstandings, the "diehards" who remained on the farm tried to keep up their spirits. After work they hunted and organized expeditions, visiting, among other places, Santiago Canyon, not far from Anaheim, where they spent the night in a cabin on the mountain.

At this time another feature of Rudolph's character manifested itself—the desire to use time in a rational manner. This trait no doubt had a main role in his later successes.

At the beginning of 1877 he joined his mother in San Francisco, and he took part in the English lessons, while his mother was preparing to play the roles of Adrienne Lecouvreur, and Shakespeare's Juliet at the California Theatre. Rudolph made rapid strides in acquiring the English language. In March he wrote a skit, and with the sons of the former governor of Washington Territory, Edward S. Salomon, performed it at their home. Chłapowski's social position made such contacts possible.

Despite contacts at high places in society, they lived very frugally for several months, often making use of the pawnshop. It was a difficult period of humiliation and uncertainty. There were moments when Helena thought of returning to Warsaw. She wrote to the manager of the theater there, but in reply received a letter stating that her services were no longer required. What could she do? She had to stake all on one throw—and succeed.

At this time Rudolph continued to study English and practice the piano; he was the first in the group to master the new language. His mother later recalled that his music "helped to bring out the poetic qualities of Shakespeare's texts." In his free time he took his mother and Johanna "Jo" Tucholsky, their English teacher, boating on Oakland Bay. They rowed to Yerba Buena Island, in the center of the bay, or on good days went all the way to Oakland. Who would have thought at the time that this bay would eventually be crossed by one of the world's great bridges with Rudolph playing a major role in its construction!

At this time Helena Modrzejewska changed her last name by removing a few letters, to Modjeska. She did this on the recommendation of John

McCullough, director of the California Theater, who was convinced that the original spelling was a tongue-breaker for Americans. Her son changed his surname as well, and abandoned Rudolph, in favor of the more American version, Ralph.

Adapting to the change of name came easily to him. Possibly, at the time he did not know, but might have instinctively sensed, that the name Modrzejewski was only an artistic prop. After Helena's great success in San Francisco, documented in enthusiastic correspondence of Henryk Sienkiewicz and later published in the *Gazeta Polska* in Warsaw,[1] Modjeska began her first artistic tour of the American west. Ralph accompanied her on the tour, but a sixteen-year-old son did not fit well into the entourage of the youthful star. For the sake of appearances he presented himself as her younger brother, and stated to reporters that he was born ten years after his "sister."

He made good use of his time. In addition to helping his mother study for her parts he worked on perfecting his linguistic and musical talents. The promoter of the tour through the cities and towns of California and Nevada was an Irish actor, James M. Ward, a veteran player in troupes touring the West. A colorful man, he was an archetype for characters that would later appear in Western films. Helena accepted his invitation to join the tour since it would help her to improve her English and Ralph was eager to see more of the West. Visits to mining towns must have been a treat to a young man interested in engineering.

It was probably Ralph's presence that, during their stay in Virginia City, Nevada, influenced the entire touring company to take a trip into the underground workings of the Consolidated Virginia Silver Mine. Modjeska's stage success there and the visit in the mine were both colorfully described by Sienkiewicz, who followed them there a few weeks later.

During her second tour the actress visited the East Coast where at the end of February she and Ralph were invited to the home of Henry Wadsworth Longfellow at Canterbury near Boston. Her son played a Chopin nocturne for the renowned poet.

At this time Modjeska wrote home to Warsaw from Philadelphia,

> Ralph is not going to study music. He loves music and plays because there are few other things to do. In a few months he will return to school in Poland, while Karol and I will probably go to the Paris Exposition. The stay in America will help Ralph in his future career. He has learned the language and can find his way about here.... He does want to return because he wants to be present at the digging of the Panama Canal. He will study to be an engineer.

After her second tour Modjeska, now with fame and financial security, left for Europe with her husband. They visited Ireland, spent a short time in London, and four weeks in Paris. In August of 1878 they arrived in Kraków, where Helena was received with honors just short of those reserved for national heroes.

On the return trip the Chłapowskis again stopped in Paris. The actress had her portrait painted and ordered theatrical costumes. But her main reason for being there was to visit her son. In June, Chłapowski wrote to his sister in Kopaszew that Ralph would stay in Kraków to continue his studies, yet over the next few months the decision changed. Ralph would go to France and study there.

Kraków by then must have seemed like a very cramped place. At that time the province of Galicia was impoverished, with little industry, and opportunities for an education and a career in engineering were not good.

Only a year earlier a Polytechnic Institute was established in Lwów becoming the first and only engineering school for forty years where the official language used for teaching was Polish. While it evolved to become a leading institution, at its beginning, however, the standard of education was not high. Ralph's ambitions (and those of his mother) could be better satisfied in Paris, where the Ecole des Ponts and Chaussées (School for Bridges and Roads) had established a 100-year reputation in training civil engineers.

It was an important decision. The choice of a profession and a place to study, and ultimately the choice of country, had great ramifications. In a way, it was also a choice of the era in which he was to live. There were tremendous differences between the United States, already aiming at the twentieth century, and Galicia, a part of the Austro-Hungarian Empire, which in the late nineteenth century still remained firmly rooted in the eighteenth century when it came to social and economic dimensions.

One cannot understate the enormous effect that this choice had on Ralph Modjeski's life. For years

Main entrance to the Ecole des Ponts et Chaussées.

he inhabited two different worlds. He moved from one to the other with ease, and they permeated all his endeavors. In the family circle of Helena Modjeska Polish customs and traditions, created over centuries, predominated. Under these each person followed an assigned and unambiguous path—an arrangement that, even for an active and energetic person, was difficult to modify. But in America the economic and social conditions of a new industrial society were in flux. In America there were few rigid traditions or historical limitations; nearly anything was possible. Here accomplishment was what counted. Personal initiative was valued at a level far above that known in Poland or elsewhere in Europe.

Modjeski, by choosing to study at the Ecole des Ponts et Chaussées, was not the first Pole to enter that school. Ernest Malinowski, an alumnus of the school in the 1840s, was already building imposing bridges and tunnels on the world's highest rail line through the Peruvian Andes. Two other Polish engineers, Edward Habich and Władysław Kluger, were employed in South America as well. Stanisław Kierbedź was building great bridges in the far reaches of the Russian Empire. A hundred years earlier, Tadeusz Kościuszko as a young and

poor student on a small stipend from King Stanisław August Poniatowski and Prince Adam Czartoryski, made his way to Paris to study under Jean-Rodolphe Perronet, who later headed the Ecole des Ponts et Chaussées. Later, Kościuszko would demonstrate his engineering skills in America as one of Washington's generals.

Helena left her son in the care of her friend, Anna Wolska, who lived for years in France. Half Polish, half American, Wolska served as a kind of agent for Helena in Paris maintaining contact with dress designer Madame Duluc. (In the summer of 1878 Helena spent 2,000 dollars on Paris fashions).

On August 20 Ralph bade his parents farewell on the Cherbourg dock as they left for America, then he returned to Paris to study for the rigorous entrance examination of the famous civil engineering school.

Austrian schools of the time were not the most modern, but gave their students a good general education. A graduate would be able to speak publicly and write well. He would have received a grounding in the humanities, necessary to anyone who wanted to get on in life. Ralph's knowledge, acquired in Kraków and supplemented by home study in America, was equivalent to the level required of Austrian middle school graduates. He knew languages and geography, but there were gaps, especially in scientific subjects.

The stay in Paris fired the imagination of the future engineer. The city was the cultural capital of the world and a center of technological progress. Great buildings and wide streets, designed by Georges Eugene Hausmann, gave Paris a character totally different from that of any other large metropolis of the time.[2] Evidence of the recent Franco-Prussian War and the social unrest which followed were nearly gone, and the city was preparing for a great World Exposition.

The famous engineer Gustav Eiffel, a builder of many spectacular structures, including the world's largest arch bridge over the Duero River in Portugal, had just completed a great department store *Au Bon Marché*, possibly the first such edifice on the continent. His 300-meter iron tower in Paris was nearing completion. After seventeen months of construction it became the tallest and most impressive construction of the nineteenth century, and would stand as the tallest man-made structure until the opening of the Empire State Building forty-two years later.

The tower grew before Ralph's eyes. He lived nearby and passed it daily on his way to school. No doubt this structure, built for the soon-to-open Paris Exhibition, impressed and influenced the young student.

Due to the year-long break in his education and the differences in study programs in the Austrian and French schools, Ralph's studies took the form of individual tutoring. It was an expensive way to learn but for the only son of the "star of two continents" it was affordable. For a while, just before taking the entrance exam, he attended the finest middle school in Paris, L'institution Duvigneau de Lanneau on the Rue de Rennes.

A year passed before he saw his beloved and admired mother again, in June 1879. Ralph was pleased by the news that through Henry Wadsworth Longfellow, Modjeska had managed to obtain a letter of introduction for him to Ferdinand de Lesseps, builder of the Suez Canal from whom he hoped to receive assistance in obtaining admission to the Ecole des Ponts et Chaussées. Modjeska's visit to Europe resulted from an invitation to participate in the observances in Kraków of the 50th anniversary of Józef Ignacy Kraszewski's writing career. Ralph was also present at these festivities, as his mother arranged especially for his trip from Paris.

Kraków was a city that knew how to celebrate important anniversaries. The jubilee became a great patriotic festival attracting people from Poland's three partition zones. At Wawel Castle, overlooking the city, the great bell "Zygmunt" tolled; from the tower of St. Mary's Church the trumpeter sounded a traditional Polish air. The populace funded a statue to the poet Adam Mickiewicz. A National Museum was inaugurated. Henryk Siemiradzki donated a splendid curtain to the theatre where Helena performed as Adrienne Lecouvreur—in Polish for the first time in four years. At the great ball given at the Renaissance Cloth Hall in the city's great market square, she and the city's mayor led the Polonaise. Caught up in the general enthusiasm, Tadeusz Ajdukiewicz promised to paint her a formal portrait. This second Modjeska portrait, finished a year later shows the forty-year-old actress in the bloom of beauty and at the peak of her career. The portrait also shows her great resemblance to Helena Sanguszko, who by some accounts may have been her half-sister.

Over the next three years she made appearances

Helena Modjeska, portrait by Tadeusz Ajdukiewicz.

in Europe, mainly in Poland (Kraków, Warsaw, Lwów, Poznań, Tarnów and other cities). She spent six months in England, appearing mainly in London.

Her stage performances were spaced to allow periods for rest. July and August of 1879 were spent in Zakopane; July of 1880 was spent in the fishing town of Cadgwith near Lizard Point, Cornwall, with Ralph and several friends. That year Ralph went to Zakopane for the first time without his famous mother. His dancing successes were reported to Helena by Karol Estricher.

The following year (1881) was an unfortunate one for Ralph, nearly bringing a change in his career goals. He was not accepted at the civil engineering school. Out of more than 100 applicants for the twenty-five places available for new students at the Ecole des Ponts et Chaussées, Ralph placed twenty-seventh, narrowly missing admission. One can understand his bitter disappointment—with his artistic temperament he took the news of not being accepted very hard. For a time he considered abandoning engineering altogether and taking up a musical career. This would have been a natural course of action for him. He had mastered the piano already, under the instruction of Kazimierz Hoffman—a composer and professor at the Kraków conservatory, who was a brilliant interpreter of Chopin's works. Under his guidance Ralph's inborn musical talent had flourished. Such talents were common in Ralph's family and they were not considered extraordinary, but rather as a way of making a living.

Many years later, in an interview for the American musical monthly *The Etude* from March 1926 Modjeski stated

> It was my good fortune to have an excellent musical training in my childhood. My father was musically inclined but not a musician. My mother played the piano unusually well and had a beautiful singing voice. In fact, she had expected at one time to become an opera singer instead of a tragedienne. My piano lessons began at the age of ten, and since that time I have never been without contact with music in my life.

During the sea voyage to America and during a six-month stay there, he vacillated between engineering and music. He continued his mathematical studies, however and again sat for the entrance examination in Paris.

On his second attempt he passed the exam with flying colors. He was accepted to the Ecole des Ponts et Chaussées on October 27, 1882, with the fourth highest entrance score. His mother wrote in her journal "A great cause for happiness! Ralph passed the exam for the Ecole des Ponts et Chaussées. My dear boy writes of his great fear, not for himself, but that he would disappoint me if it all did not go well."

So in this internal struggle for one of two different career orientations, music lost out to engineering. It may also be added that a friend of later life, the pianist Ignacy Jan Paderewski, lost a potential rival.

Forty years later Ralph Modjeski, as a famous sixty-year-old engineer, remembered this time:

> I came to a decision as to what I wanted and what I was capable of attaining. I moved forward toward that moment forcefully following my chosen path and as a result received my diploma as a top student in 1885. I understand that one must not give up too easily. I told myself "Go and check if you are really following the wrong path before you turn back." It is as good a maxim as "Be sure of choosing the right path and follow it to its conclusion."

In France the significance of the linkage between theory and hundreds of years of practical engineering experience was appreciated early. In 1666 Jean Baptiste Colbert founded the Academie des Sciences thereby securing for France a leading position in the development of engineering knowledge. As France's economy developed, roads and bridges were needed. During the reign of Louis XV, in 1716, the army engineering officer corps supplied the first members of the Corps des Ingenieurs des Ponts and Chaussées—the first civilian organization whose purpose was to develop road and bridge building.

From the start, this organization was very efficient. One example of its influence was a great bridge, of eleven elliptical arches, erected across the River Loire in Blois, finished in 1724. This bridge was used for 220 years, proving the high level of ability present in the Corps, especially of its chief, Jacques Gabriel.

Thirty years later this dynamic organization gave rise to the Ecole des Ponts et Chaussées—the world's first civil engineering school. For nearly fifty years the school's head and driving force was Jean Rodolphe Perronet (1708–1794) a great bridge builder who would go down in history. He was the first to use calculations—derived from the sciences of statics and strength of materials—which enabled him to build structures so bold that they can only be described as visionary. The arches of consecutive bridges he designed became flatter and thinner, the supporting piers more slender. In the Pont de Neuilly he reduced the thickness of supporting piers to one-twelfth of the span length which was half of the standard then in use. This reduction was possible only because he had worked out the mathematical relationships—using the principles of statics—of the forces acting on the spans, and applied the appropriate method of removing the supporting scaffolding. He went even further when he designed and executed his last work, at age eighty—the Pont de la Concorde, the famous and still admired bridge in the heart of Paris.

The experience of Perronet and his contemporaries developed and expanded over the next 100 years, especially in the theory of construction and building with stone, and later concrete. The school Ralph chose had a very high level of professionalism.

Among the lecturers at the school, when Ralph attended it, was Aime Henri Résal, a pioneer in steel construction and author of the manual *Traite de Mécanique Générale*, used by several generations of engineers not only in France but around the world. Lectures on bridge construction were presented by M. Croizette-Desnoyers and J. Choix. Ralph's recitation sessions were led by the young Paul Sejourne, already well known for his practical achievements. It is easy to see how a school with such teachers could inspire a fascination in a young student for bridges, which enable man to overcome the geographic constraints of his environment, connect with that which was previously unreachable, and conquer the obstacles posed by nature.

During this period, as before, Helena often saw her son and took an active interest in his life. In December 1881, travelling to see her mother in Kraków, she stopped to see him in Paris. At that time Ralph was going through the preparatory courses for the Ecole des Ponts et Chaussées exam. A few months later, in April 1882, she was again in Paris for several weeks, shopping and ordering new gowns. The following year Ralph went to California, proud of his accomplishment as the top student in his class. In *Memories and Impressions* Modjeska writes that they spent their vacation together "very happily" visiting the home of Joseph Pleasants and his family in Santiago Canyon, California, their friends from the time of the Anaheim farm.

In that time the family spent over two months together crossing the continent, visiting Denver, Yellowstone Park, and New Mexico en route to Los Angeles and Anaheim. On July 3, 1883, in Los Angeles, Karol Chłapowski and Ralph became United States citizens. A small group of close friends dined with them at the Pico Hotel to celebrate the occasion.[3] Ralph left them in mid-August while they were in Chicago. His mother resumed her theatrical work; he returned to school.

In 1884 the summer vacation was again a group holiday, this time partly in Brittany, France and

Felicie Benda, a photograph from the time of her stay at the boarding school in Walmer, Kent.

partly in Kraków and Zakopane. There were good reasons for making the trip, for Helena's half-brother Adolph Opid, the only one in that family who did not go on the theatrical stage, had built a beautiful villa for the Chłapowskis on the side of Antalówka Mountain, on the property now called Modrzejów. For five weeks the house was full of music and song. Paderewski was there and Helena was in her element among family and numerous guests.

She especially noticed and took a liking to Felicie Benda the beautiful blonde daughter of her half-brother Felix Benda, who was an actor. She took the girl under her care and at the beginning of 1882 sent her to a Catholic convent school operated by an order of Polish nuns in Walmer, county Kent, England. So that the young girl would not be totally alone Helena also sent Józefina Tomaszewicz, a cousin, to the school, where the two girls would remain for three years. Anna Wolska, still residing in Paris, would be the adult supervising the two girls.

During the summer, the two young ladies and their chaperone visited London, and spent a few

15

weeks in Cornwall with Helena. Ralph was there as well.

Overall, Modjeska's influence on family matters was great. Her success, fame, and money seemed to have given her a mandate to rule all that was within her reach. It would have been exceptional if Ralph had evaded this influence.

She also had a very strong sense of family solidarity. She helped all her relations, not counting the time, effort, money. On the stage she was an actress, but in the family she was the choreographer. It may be said that she deliberately arranged to bring Felicie Benda and her son Ralph together, both in Cornwall and, the following summer in Zakopane.

Modjeska continued to extend her care over her future daughter-in-law, who was six years younger than Ralph. In a letter from Milwaukee dated February 1883, she asks Anna Wolska to return to Poland and keep an eye on Felicie. She writes quite directly, "I fear for Felicie, that someone might turn her head too early." In another letter she asks "please, never let Felicie out of your sight and do not take her to any parties."

During Ralph's last year of study she traveled in Europe with the energy that was her trademark. At the beginning of the year she gave performances in Kraków and Warsaw, arousing the enthusiasm of theater patrons and critics alike. In March she performed in London, then in other English cities and in Ireland.

Wherever she went, she carried on a very active social life. At the height of her fame, despite her age she still was beautiful, admired, and very much desired. She behaved like a queen, and like a queen she dispensed favors.

In October of 1884 she introduced Ignacy Jan Paderewski as a concert pianist, organizing a recital at the beautiful Saski Hotel in Kraków. Young and handsome, and already a superb pianist he made a wonderful impression, a compliment to his patroness. It was also his first step onto a larger stage. The room in which he played had seen Liszt and Brahms, and was a place where the best of Kraków society gave elaborate balls. The money from the receipts opened the way to Europe for the young artist.

Felicie Benda had been in Kraków since summer's end. Her journal contains notes, in Polish and French, for the first months of 1885. Through them we can see a sober, thoughtful girl, private in her thoughts, mainly interested in social life. In February she went to Paris with her aunt, where she spent several weeks. Her description of the visit to the dress shop of Madame Duluc is rather long, yet her future husband gets only one line: "Ralph met us at the station."

Gustav Zimajer was also interested in the progress of Ralph's education. At this time he resided in Berlin. Before Ralph's graduation he sent him his photograph with the dedication "To my dear son Rudolph, whom I love above life itself. From Father." The photograph is dated February 16, 1885. It appears that the old tensions—over time—had lessened, for Modjeska had congratulated (by telegram) Zimajer's wife, Adolfina, on her success in Berlin's musical theater. Ralph saw his father and kept up the contact through a frequent exchange of letters.

There is also evidence that Ralph maintained contact with his father's new family— notably with his half-sister Helena. Adolfina, who became a star of the musical theater, the toast of Warsaw, Vienna, Berlin and other European cities, had an excellent rapport with Ralph while her daughter Helena,[4] appears to have worshiped him. There is a warm interview given by Helena (then married and using the surname Rapacka) about her relationship with her half-brother. A photograph illustrating this published interview shows Zimajer, his young wife and Ralph—about eighteen or nineteen years old at the time.

On July 6, 1885, Ralph received his diploma as engineer of roads and bridges. As his thesis work he designed a steel bridge crossing an American river. He had prepared well for his future career. Each year he earned the best marks, and passed the final examinations with distinction among the top students in the class. He shared his happiness with his mother when she came to Paris from Dublin at the end of her third British tour. They traveled together to Kraków, then to Zakopane where on the Modrzejów estate a grand engagement ceremony of Ralph and Felicie took place. Guests included Paderewski, Chałubiński, and, of course, the faithful Anna Wolska.[5]

In September, after a month-long visit in Poland, the family sailed for New York. During October, November, and December Modjeska continued her eighth tour in America taking Felicie with her. A special train took her and her retinue across America. Each appearance was a flurry of applause, flowers, and press interviews. The tour was a tremendous artistic and financial success.

Meanwhile, Ralph began work as an engineer-in-training in Omaha, Nebraska, where a bridge was being built across the Missouri River. His mother continued to run his affairs. She came to Omaha, where she was impressed with the picturesque setting of the city, praised the fresh country air, and found him an apartment.

The day of the long-awaited wedding drew close. On December 20, 1885, a New York paper printed the following article:

> Next Wednesday Modjeska's only son, just 21,[6] will marry his cousin Felicie Benda in the Polish Catholic Church. To do so he had to have a special dispensation from the Pope. He is in the Chief Engineer's Department of the Chicago, Burlington and Quincy Railroad and has come from Omaha, for a month's leave.

Later in the article its author described Felicie as a beautiful blonde-haired girl with a proud bearing.

Ralph and Felicie were married on December 28 at St. Stanisław's Church, located in a working-class neighborhood in New York City, almost in the shadow of the Brooklyn Bridge.

It was an unusual choice. Helena could have had the pick of any church in the city including St. Patrick's Cathedral, which would have gladly opened its doors. She belonged to the upper reaches of society, and was among those who have managed to attain a high standing on the first attempt. She had fame and money, and no door was closed to her.

The ceremony was also unusual. As noon neared, a line of sumptuous carriages appeared on narrow, dirty Stanton Street of the lower East Side. This immediately caused a great commotion. Along the entrance steps, a row of formally attired members of the St. Stanisław Society, held lighted candles. Behind them stood a second row of men, dressed in military uniforms, each holding a saber. *The New York Times* on December 29, reported that these were "fantastic Polish uniforms in red and yellow colors."

The bride was led from the carriage to the altar by two young unmarried men, E.S. Nadal and Joseph Gilder, while the groom was accompanied by two single ladies (the Thurston sisters of Buffalo). Father Klimuski (Klimecki), pastor of St. Stanisław's officiated, while Archbishop Corrigan

Felicie and Ralph Modjeski, wedding photo. Courtesy of Halka Chronic.

gave a sermon appropriate to the occasion.

After the ceremony the order of things was reversed: two married men led Felicie from the church, while two married women accompanied Ralph. There was no lack of press descriptions of the participants and their outfits. "The bride wore a rather conventional gown of white satin with a long tulle veil," wrote one correspondent, "decorated with orange blossoms. She did not look to be 20 years old,[7] while the groom looked to be much more mature."

The main choreographer of this performance, the famous mother, appeared in a blue satin gown paired with a bright brocade stole. The reporter did not fail to notice that this dress was made in Paris and that its owner had worn it in the first act of *Odette*.

When the ceremony ended the wedding party and guests departed for Delmonico's on the corner of 26th Street and Broadway,[8] New York's most elegant and expensive restaurant. The curious and neighborhood well-wishers who attended the ceremony were not forgotten: a buffet, well supplied in sandwiches and beer, was set up for them in the church basement.

After the reception, Ralph and Felicie honeymooned in New Orleans. Returning to Omaha, they moved into a house given to them as a wedding present by Ralph's mother.

Despite an exhausting schedule of performances Helena found time to write to them regularly. She continued to be interested in their welfare, as is shown in her letter dated January 12, 1886.

> My dear son and my dear daughter-in-law! I barely found a moment today to write to you though I don't have any news, as your father tells you everything. We are longing for a few words from you and hope that you will write from Omaha about your health and the happenings in your household.
>
> In a few days Walman will be in Omaha. I entrusted him with a Japanese vase and a bracelet which father sent for Felicie. There is also an amber hair comb from Thurston, which Felicie had forgotten. I trust these things will reach you in good order. I have picked out your bed linen and tablecloths, choosing the best quality I could. I could not find the small sheets for the maid, but this can easily be done. I did buy a blanket for her bed, which it seems Ralph had forgotten. The embroidered bedspread with pillow covers is an additional gift from me to Felicie. I am sending pink satin for the lining, knowing that the bedroom is decorated in pink. I think you will have plenty of curtains, while the warm down comforter will no doubt prove to be indispensable.

The letter communicates an exceptional level of interest and care. Despite intense work, the loving mother seems to remember everything. The gifts no doubt were a godsend, for the young engineer, in his first professional assignment, was earning very little. A fifty-dollar monthly salary at that time could buy much more than it can now, but in his social position it meant comparative poverty.

A few weeks later, at the end of January 1886, Helena wrote to her friend Karol Estricher in Kraków.

> I married off my son and the happy couple now reside in the state of Nebraska, where Ralph is employed as an assistant in building a bridge on the Missouri River. He will remain there until the bridge is completed, that is for two years.

The key phrase is "I married off" and it reveals Helena's attitude. What the newly married couple thought and felt about being dominated had not been articulated so far. But it may have had an effect on their relationship later.

Chapter 3

Beginning a Career

Young Ralph Modjeski was destined for success. When in October of 1885 he started to work with George Morison he was probably one of the best theoretically prepared engineers in the New World. His preparation for a professional career was based on a wide area of study, with a strong foundation of general knowledge and humanities.

His character traits have been mentioned before. His mother's assistance during his early professional life enabled him to learn the practical basics of his profession without worrying about day-to-day necessities.

Most important to Ralph's career was the person of his employer, George Shattuck Morison, at this time the leading builder of bridges in America. Not quite fifty years old, Morison was at the zenith of his creative abilities. Working with this intelligent and experienced engineer, later called the "Father of American Bridge Building"[1] in the *Transactions of the American Society of Civil Engineers*, gave Modjeski the practical experience that in a few years allowed him to successfully undertake and execute projects of extreme scale and difficulty.

Ralph got his job through connections but quickly showed that he had all the requirements to be a good engineer. Morison was a hands-on builder, but understood that large bridges of the near future would require a good understanding of theory as a basis for design. Therefore, he must have appreciated the above average abilities and character traits of his young intern.

The first bridge on whose construction Modjeski was employed was a large one and required his full engagement. It was a steel railroad bridge over the Missouri River at Omaha, Nebraska built for the Union Pacific Railroad.

Modjeski worked for Morison for seven years (1885–1892) beginning with a two-year assignment in the shops which produced steel sections for the bridge. There he was able to learn the possibilities and limitations of prefabricating elements in the shops, and received a good grounding for later employment in the design office—the type of knowledge that cannot be learned in any school.

In the succeeding two years Modjeski worked in the design office, advancing to the position of chief draftsman. During this time Morison designed a Mississippi River bridge to be built near Memphis, Tennessee. Then during the years 1891–1892 he was an inspector (quality control) in shops that fabricated the steel elements for this bridge. Subsequently he spent a year as assistant to the engineer who directed assembly of the load-bearing portions of the bridge. The largest cantilever bridge built up to that date in the western hemisphere, the Memphis Bridge had five spans (56, 230, 189, 184, and 106 meters or 184, 755, 620, 604, 348 feet respectively). The only longer spans then in existence were in the Firth of Forth Bridge in Scotland and at Sukkur on the Indus River in India (now in Pakistan). In later years Modjeski would conduct a renovation of the bridge at Memphis.

The years that Modjeski spent with Morison could be counted as an extension of his schooling. The internship was exemplary. If one had wanted to design a training program for a young engineer who wanted to specialize in steel construction, one could not do better than what Morison did for his intern.

Modjeski could give all his attention to his professional work because life for the young couple, during this first period, was going well. His famous mother regularly visited their modest home at 2308 Burt Street in Omaha. In May 1886 she spent three weeks there, and all of August and part of Septem-

George Morison's bridge at Omaha, Nebraska, built during Ralph Modjeski's apprenticeship. A contemporary postcard.

ber in the following year. This longer stay followed the birth of Felix, Ralph and Felicie's first child, named in memory of Felix Benda, his grandfather. Helena wrote to Anna Wolska in Paris, "Now I am on vacation with Ralph, Felicie and little Felix, who was born on August 6 at 6 a.m. He is big and beautiful. I don't know yet whom he will resemble more, but it looks as though it will be Felicie." In the same letter she wrote "Ralph is very thin and pale from hard work and extremely worried over the mental and physical health of his wife."

After completion of the bridge over the Missouri in 1887 the family moved from Omaha to Athens, Pennsylvania "a city not unlike Wieliczka[2] except instead of salt they have a foundry here where Ralph works as a supervisor of work being done for the bridge." But the material conditions of the "supervisor" were slim and his mother still supplied periodic infusions of cash.

At the steel works owned and operated by the American Bridge Works Ralph was a supervisor of quality control for elements being fabricated in the shops for Morison's construction office. This new work was so demanding and absorbing for Ralph that in the large Victorian house in which they lived, Felicie was virtually by herself. Athens was a typical American town where the tight social spheres were not friendly to outsiders and she may have felt isolated and lonely there. Customs different from those to which she was accustomed, poor knowledge of the language, a husband who was constantly at work, and an inadequate income made adjustment difficult, possibly introducing the first cracks in the marriage.

In 1890 the Modjeskis traveled to Europe where they visited Paris, and spent the summer with family in Kraków and Zakopane. Little Felix was two years old and just learning to talk. His primary language was English for his nanny was an American.

During the stay in Poland Ralph met with his father, now sixty-five years old and probably also with his half-sister Helena, eight years younger than he. The Zimajers most likely lived in Warsaw at the time, since that summer Helena Zimajer appeared at the Bagatela Theater in the city.

Helena Modjeska was also in Poland during this time. There is no information if she had ever met Zimajer again after making her departure in Czerniowiec, however in 1893 she wrote to Józef Kotarbiński, director of the Kraków theater, recommending Helena Zimajer to him.

In 1889 Modjeski moved to Chicago to work at

20

Marylka, Karolek, and Felix — the Modjeski children. Courtesy of Halka Chronic.

the main office of Morison's design bureau. The city was developing at a faster rate than most American cities and in a few years became the industrial and financial center of the Midwest. The astounding pace of its growth contributed to the creation of the Chicago School, a group of builders and architects, among them Louis Sullivan, John Root, and the young Frank Lloyd Wright whose initiative prompted the erection of a group of buildings in mid-town towering between 60–80 meters (197–262 feet) in height—the world's first skyscrapers. One of these was Monadnock Building, designed by John Root and placed on the corner of Dearborn and Jackson Streets. Simple in form and without excessive ornamentation it is probably the tallest brick structure in the world.[3] It became a Chicago landmark, indicator of the city's resilience and drive toward the next century. In a few years Ralph Modjeski's engineering offices and apartment would be located at this address.

Monadnock Building was, as the new century approached, the largest and finest building in Chicago, if not in the United States. To have an office or an apartment there indicated a rise

upward both figuratively and literally. Knowing how Americans always wanted to be on top of things, was it instinct that caused Modjeski to seek offices there?

Modjeska visited her son whenever possible. In 1892 she was in Chicago several times. They spent the Christmas holidays around the family table, "just like in Poland"—with the traditional Christmas singing, tree, and Polish food. Four weeks later Felicie gave birth to a daughter, baptized Maria Stuart Helena, because on the day of her birth her grandmother was playing in Schiller's *Maria Stuart*. She was soon nicknamed Marylka, a Polish diminutive of Maria, also the name of Ralph's long-dead sister.

A reporter from a Chicago newspaper noted on the social page that the baby was baptized at the Polish Church of St. Stanisław Kostka, and that Piotr Kiołbasa, president of the Polish Roman-Catholic Union—the main Polish-American organization—was the godfather. Countess Łubieńska was the godmother.

After his seven-year apprenticeship with Morison the thirty-year-old Modjeski struck out on his

The Government Bridge at Rock Island, Illinois. The bridge has a large rotating span that allows river vessels to navigate on the waterway. Photograph courtesy of Jan Plachta.

own. Seeking to become independent, he went into partnership with S. Nicholson and established an engineering project and consulting office in Chicago in the following year. This was a time of economic uncertainty in the United States and there was not much work. The small projects on which he worked during this time gave him no satisfaction, while the financial results were far from expectations. The partnership was dissolved. His mother wrote during this time, "it was a very bad year and Ralph has been without work for over a year-and-a-half, while maintaining a household costs them four to five thousand dollars a year." She of course, assisted them as she had done before.

Finally, in 1895 Modjeski received his first large contract, a project to design and supervise construction of a bridge over the Mississippi at Rock Island, Illinois. A milestone in the life of the young engineer and salvation for a man living in near poverty, it was also a major event for his mother, who wrote to Anna Wolska "This contract has opened the way to a future career."

The bridge at Rock Island, built for the United States Government and the Chicago, Rock Island and Pacific Railway Company, was a combined rail and highway bridge. A truss construction, it had several simple supported spans with parallel chords. The total length of the bridge (measuring from the extreme support points) was 1,871 feet (about 600 meters). In addition, the project included buildings and warehouses for the nearby military arsenal, one of the few non-bridge jobs done by Modjeski.

The work was highly absorbing. During the mounting of the load-bearing members of the structure Modjeski was almost continuously in Davenport, Iowa, seven hours by train from Chicago, only occasionally able to return home for a day or two.

Helena Modjeska wrote with motherly pride in a letter from California dated December 29, 1896, "Ralph is finishing his bridge and looking for new work. He received high praise from the engineering commission which gathered to inspect the bridge. All unanimously agreed that Ralph's plans and execution were first-rate engineering work, and his picture appeared in the papers."

The Rock Island Bridge was the first of a series of large bridges built under his supervision, or that of his firm, over the next 40 years.

The timing was favorable to bridge building in the United States. The infrastructure of the United

States was developing rapidly, especially in transportation. In a country where distances were great and rivers large, constructing railroads and bridging rivers became extremely important. Railroad expansion progressed at a breakneck pace. During the decade 1880–1890 the amount of track in the United States grew by 70 thousand miles, or had nearly doubled. Between 1869 and the turn of the century four transcontinental lines went into operation.

Henryk Sienkiewicz traveled to California in 1876, probably one of the first Poles to undertake a crossing of the continent by rail, a venture not altogether without risks. If he was not the first Pole to do so, he certainly was the first to write detailed stories about it in Polish. When all went well the trip from New York to San Francisco by special train lasted less than four days. The difficulties in making the trip were many: bad track, unfriendly Indians, weather, etc. It was a trip for those who had the will and courage to travel.

Many of those who traveled west of the Mississippi were propelled by Horace Greeley's words "Go west young man, go west!" To stay in place was to loose ground! Ralph Modjeski was young, he had the internal qualities that fit the motto, and he was able to take an active role in pushing the rails toward the Pacific.

One should then not be surprised that the rush for building large, which typified America at the end of the nineteenth century, pulled him along. He adopted an engineer's mindset, thinking in terms of the "big picture." He evaluated the problems of large structures in terms of the role they would play in the overall economy. In addition to his personal qualities, the romance of building on a grand scale also influenced the results of his work.

Steel was just beginning to be used in large quantities in the building of American bridges. James B. Eads first used it as the material for a significant number of the load-carrying members in his great bridge at St. Louis. And by 1880 there also was a large bridge on the Missouri that was built mainly of this new material. In the 1890s when the price of steel fell, it displaced wrought iron as an economically useful structural material. Modjeski was the first engineer who started his professional career building bridges with steel as the material of choice. From the very first day of employment he continued to gather knowledge and experience in this field.

Felicie Modjeski with the children, Marylka, Felix, and Karolek. Photograph courtesy of Halka Chronic.

Modjeski played a direct part in enlarging the railroad network of the United States by constructing bridges across large rivers. His pioneering solutions were used as examples by others. He himself created the right conditions for this to happen. Between 1898 and 1900 he compiled *Standard Designs for Steel Bridges*, a set of designs and specifications for steel bridges with spans that varied from 10 to 250 feet. Produced for the Northern Pacific Railroad, his was the first such manual published in the United States. It fulfilled its purpose for many years.

In December of 1888, able to approach bridge projects as an engineer who had achieved professional recognition he became an Associate Member of the American Society of Civil Engineers (ASCE) the main civil engineering association in the United States whose president was George Morison, his employer. He had been a Junior Member since 1886.

The bridge at Thebes, Illinois. Photograph courtesy of Modjeski and Masters, Inc.

Helena Modjeska mentioned her son's professional involvement to Maria Chłapowska in a letter dated February 4, 1900.

> Ralph has a good occupation, but I can't really describe it. All I know is that in his office he employs and supervises eight to twelve people. From this I deduct that he has a lot of work. He does work for many railroads, drawing up plans for bridges and then supervising their construction. He is healthy, has gained weight and looks good. He is always overly gentle and patient ...

On March 29, 1896, a family gathering took place in Ralph's home—located in an enclave of private houses in the so-called better section of Chicago—at 1177 North Clark Street.

The First Lady of the Theater, as the press picturesquely called Helena Modjeska, had to cancel her eighteenth tour because of illness. So she took the opportunity to visit her son's home at the beginning of February 1896 eager to see her third grandchild, Charles Emmanuel John (nicknamed Karolek). The baptism was a ceremonial affair; his godparents were famous singers, soloists at the Metropolitan Opera, Emma Calvé and Jan Reszke. Charles' older brother was ten, his sister was three.

At this time there was an incident about which there is little information. Shortly after the baby was born Ralph received a series of threatening let-

ters. In March someone had tried to kidnap Marylka during a walk outside. There was also a harmless, amateurish attempt to break into the house. This matter remains unexplained and without resolution.

At the end of the year Helena described Ralph's children in the following way.

> Felix (Dodo) goes to school, and takes instruction in religion from the priest, whom he visits three times a week. He is becoming quite a serious young man, not unlike his father. Marylka is not pretty, but well developed for her age, and talented. Ralph expects much joy from her in the future. She will be four in January. The youngest, Karolek is the prettiest—healthy, active, and with a good appetite.

Such tight bonds between Helena and her grandchildren lasted to the end of her life, and manifested themselves in various ways.

It is worthwhile to mention one characteristic example. One year while resting at her Arden home, Helena wrote a fairy tale for her grandchildren, which she illustrated herself. It consisted of 100 pages of English text duplicated page by page in Polish, so that the children would not forget the native language of their parents.

Family life at this time was going smoothly. Modjeski was working with great intensity, simultaneously enlarging the military facility at Rock Island and beginning the construction of a large new Mississippi River bridge at Thebes, Illinois, 36 miles from where the Ohio River joins the Mississippi.

In this period he started direct cooperation with his friend Alfred Noble, a famous engineer, and his senior by a few years. A bridge builder in his own right, Noble was also involved in large water projects; he was a member of the advisory committee during the building of the Panama Canal, and a president of the ASCE.

During 1902–1905 the firm of Noble and Modjeski completed a bridge at Thebes for the Southern Illinois and Missouri Bridge Company—a cantilever steel construction, carrying a two-track rail line. The main part of the bridge consisted of one large span 671 feet in length, two spans 521 feet 2 inches long and two 518 feet 6 inches each. The total bridge length, including the approach ramps, was 4.7 miles.[4]

The numbers may not say much to those who are not concerned with bridges on a professional level. But every engineer knows how many important decisions must be made and how much effort is required to put such a large construction into place.

The use of cantilever design in building a large bridge was a great step forward in the realm of engineering. Only a quarter-century had passed since Heinrich Gerber patented his principle and used it to build a much smaller cantilever bridge across the Main River at Hassfurt, Germany, the first such bridge of this type in the world.

In building the bridge at Thebes, especially its approach spans, Modjeski was among the first in the United States to use concrete in large quantities. To do this he had to overcome the resistance of the professional community and convince them as to the validity of this type of construction.

Some years later the French engineer Francois Hennebique built the steel reinforced concrete Risorgimento Bridge in Rome—a span of 100 meters. But Modjeski had achieved similar results several years earlier in America in building the approaches to the bridge at Thebes.

The knowledge gained at the Ecole des Ponts et Chaussées was bearing dividends. It was there that reinforced concrete was first tried. It is true, there was no regular course in this building method at the Ecole then, but in lectures on "ponts en maconnerie" there must have been mention of the bridge

RALPH MODJESKI
CIVIL ENGINEER

Sketch from the Chicago Star *in a cycle of articles "Chicagoans, As We See Them."*

built a few years earlier in the private park of the Marquis Tiliere in Chazelet near Paris. Modjeski must also have seen the 1873 patent drawings for an invention by a French gardener, Joseph Monier, which illustrated the new construction method as used in bridge arches. In any case, he had no doubts as to the correctness of his choice when he used reinforced concrete in the piers and arches of the approach spans of the Thebes bridge.

This endeavor ended in success. Testing of the bridge for strength yielded positive results. Modjeski, as chief engineer and bridge builder, showed great ingenuity and technical boldness as well as persistence in bringing his ideas to successful completion. As a result he was honored by the engineering community: the ASCE, named him Engineer of the Year and the State Assembly designated him a "Man of Illinois." The bridge and its builder were widely praised.

In the summer of 1903 Modjeski was honored as Engineer of the Year, this was the first ray of fame yet to come. The popular magazine *Chicago Star,* in a cycle of articles "Chicagoans, As We See Them," published a sketch of Modjeski standing before a map of the United States. The cartoonist overstated things. True, he had some artistic license, but this kind of correlation would be true only after a few more years had passed!

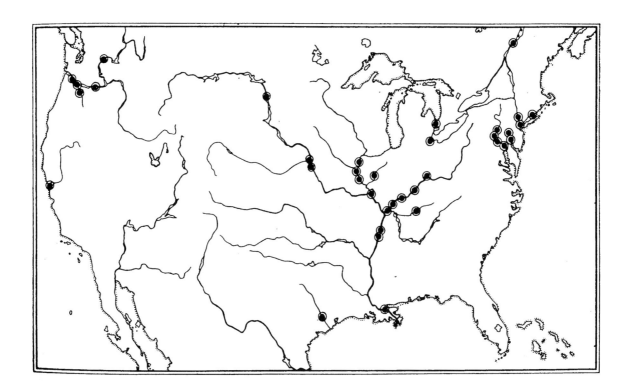

A map of the United States showing the places where Ralph Modjeski had built bridges during his long career.

Chapter 4

The Quebec Bridge

Successful completion of the bridge at Thebes, still in use today despite the increase in the loads travelling over it, was the beginning of a series of projects that Ralph Modjeski would undertake during the next thirty years in the United States (including Alaska) and Canada. With each new bridge, his knowledge and experience increased and his reputation as an authority in the professional community rose to greater heights.

Even after he became a well known engineer, his firm had to compete against other engineering concerns. These were the conditions of working in an open economy.

But there were plenty of commissions, and Modjeski won over his competitors because he was professionally competent and his firm represented the highest level of engineering achievement. He also had the ability to communicate his ideas. Among his personal qualities was an understanding of his profession on several levels and at a depth not possessed by others. His personality and behavior inspired respect. He displayed a talent for winning people over and, through logic, convincing them as to the validity of his point of view. Strangers, even those who were prejudiced against him, went away from meetings charmed and thoroughly won over. Among those around him, he could create a natural respect without arousing anger or jealousy.

Such qualities aided his building activities but were especially valuable where logistics included economic, legal, or social problems. The average engineer often does not see these problems at the beginning of a project, but Modjeski recognized and appreciated them, and thereby gained a competitive advantage.

It would serve no purpose to discuss every bridge built by Modjeski, even though from an engineering standpoint they may deserve it. Each was an achievement by its creator, whereby he conquered nature and his competition. From the long list of projects completed by Modjeski or with his active participation, we shall discuss only the most significant.

During the years 1905–1908 he conducted, as chief engineer, the reconstruction (including the replacement of load-bearing members) of a single-track railroad bridge over the Missouri River for the Northern Pacific Railway Company; the building of two large railroad bridges in Portland, Oregon over the Columbia and Willamette Rivers; and a bridge across the Illinois River at Peoria for the Central Illinois Construction Company. A look at a map of the United States will confirm that the building sites are approximately 2,000 miles apart. For many engineers this would have been a serious impediment, but for Modjeski, used to his mother's nomadic life-style, these distances were not an obstacle. He was in constant movement and almost lived in rail coaches. In one of his letters from the period, he stated that in one year he had traveled over 50 thousand miles.

During the time that these projects were being constructed, a twenty-year-old Polish engineer, Wacław Paszkowski, joined Modjeski's office in Chicago. Later he would make a mark in Poland as a builder of many imposing structures, including the approaches to the so-called Third Bridge over the Vistula now known as the Poniatowski Bridge, and leave his legacy as Professor at the Warsaw Polytechnic. He received the chance to work and receive practical training at Modjeski's firm through the good offices of his father, railway engineer Maciej Paszkowski, one of Modjeski's friends during his years in Paris.

The next large construction project built by

The McKinley Bridge over the Mississippi River at St. Louis, Missouri, built for the St. Louis Electric Bridge Company (Illinois Traction System). Contemporary postcard.

Modjeski was the McKinley Bridge, a combination highway and railway bridge over the Mississippi at St. Louis. Not far away was the theater where his mother had triumphed in Henrik Ibsen's *Nora*, and the son "proved worthy of her fame."[1] Built in three years, this impressive bridge was at the time one of the longest in North America, with a total length (including approaches) of nearly one and a quarter miles.

The distance from Chicago to St. Louis is 300 miles, a fair distance to travel in those days. Even so, Modjeski was on site at least once a week, examining all phases of the project, as was his habit. The McKinley Bridge was not the first to cross the Mississippi in this city. His old boss George Morison worked here during 1889–1890. More importantly a bridge built by James Buchanan Eads at St. Louis was the first to cross the "Father of Waters"; it was also one of the world's first great steel bridges, which, by the time Modjeski started work, had already served well for over thirty years.

To some degree then, Modjeski had to measure up to this great feat of engineering. In some ways his job was easier, for in laying the caissons for the foundation he could draw on knowledge that had been gained during the building of Eads' bridge.

Eads had used the first modern practical application of pressurized caissons during the laying of the foundations for the arches of his bridge.[2] Workers labored in a steel chamber in which the air pressure had been raised to several times that of the atmosphere to keep the water out. Thirty died from so-called "caisson disease" before the effects of high-pressure air on the human body were understood.

During the laying of the foundations for the McKinley Bridge, Modjeski observed strictly the regimen that had been laid down for working in underwater caissons. There were no serious cases of caisson disease on his project.

The McKinley Bridge was built during 1907–1909 and is of a different construction than Eads'. Instead of arches, in its main part, it consists of three large simple supported truss spans with a curved upper chord, while the remainder are simple supported truss spans having the roadway above the main chord. Each span is 125 meters (410 feet). Even though the construction is light, the

Broadway Bridge, latest span crossing Willamette River, Portland, Ore.

The Ohio River bridge at Metropolis, Illinois. Photograph courtesy of Modjeski and Masters, Inc.

Harahan Bridge at Memphis, Tennessee. Early postcard.

Railroad bridge over the Thames River at New London, Connecticut.

bridge is not particularly pleasing esthetically. When he designed the McKinley Bridge, Modjeski seems not to have risen above the trends of the time. However, the bridge is still fully functional after ninety years of service.

Evidence of Modjeski's status by this time is the fact that in 1909 he was named by the New York City Authority to a team that was to verify the design and quality of execution for a new suspension bridge linking Manhattan and Brooklyn. Doubts had surfaced because of the shock that the engineering world had experienced due to the bridge disaster in Quebec in 1907. Modjeski did this consulting work between February and September of 1909, a time difficult for him, because of the death of his mother. Yet his accuracy and the attention he put into the task were not affected.

The analysis conducted by the team that he headed, which included W. R. Weichman, Prof. J. E. Turneauve, and W. E. Angiew, approved the plans.[3] The results and a general description were published in a special work entitled *Manhattan Bridge*, by the New York City Department of Bridges. The correctness of the analysis was confirmed by time: the bridge is still in use.

After completing the McKinley Bridge, Modjeski designed and supervised construction of a number of bridges for the Oregon Trunk Railway Company in the Pacific Northwest near the Canadian border. The rail line traversed rough, unexplored terrain under primitive conditions, and in addition to the technical problems, there were many organizational problems. Among the Modjeski bridges two deserve mention: the bridge over the Columbia River near Celilo, and a bold steel arch across the canyon of the Crooked River near Bend, Oregon, the latter built 104 meters (341 feet) above the canyon floor where the use of scaffolding was impractical. Instead, the then-innovative cantilever method of construction was used on both sides of the high rocky canyon.

Many years later, Modjeski wrote about this undertaking:

> I decided that it would be most appropriate to use a two-hinged arch with a span of 340 feet … but in the first phase of construction it would be built as a three-hinged arch under its own load … Between the two extended cantilevers a key section would be inserted at the selected temperature (60° F) to close the gap. The places for the rivets were marked, the section was withdrawn

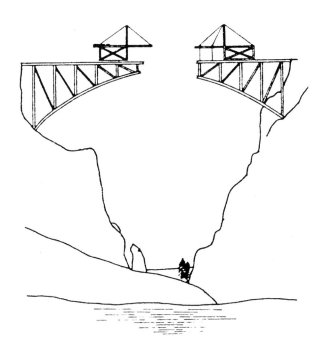

The cantilever method of assembling the Crooked River Bridge over the canyon.

and the holes drilled. Then the connecting segment was again placed into its final position and riveted in place.

In its final form the construction functions as a three-hinge arch, while for the requirements of loading and expansion due to temperature it behaves as a two-hinge arch.

The Oregon Trunk Railway Company, whose president was James Hill, was in competition with another railway company led by E. H. Harriman, for the lucrative freight travelling to and from Oregon Territory. The two companies were building nearly parallel rail lines. The spoils went to the one that crossed the Crooked River first: the Oregon Trunk Railway Company employing Modjeski.

It is impossible to describe on paper the primitive conditions, especially the situation at the Celilo work site: wild, unpopulated terrain, nature in the raw, strong, tough men. Work began in pits of treacle-like mud, then progressed upward, where workers were battered by strong wind and clouds of gritty sand. Despite the difficulties, the foundations for the Celilo bridge were finished in eleven months. Steel assembly started on April 30, 1911, and the first train crossed on January 4, 1912.[4] The entire structure consisted of eight large spans, including one that could be raised, and fourteen

Celilo Bridge on the Columbia river in Orgegon. Photograph courtesy of Jan Plachta.

shorter spans over the shallows, for a total of nearly 1,500 meters (nearly 5,000 feet). From the first shovel of earth to the first movement of traffic, only eighteen months had elapsed. Such tempo of construction is still impressive, despite the availability of modern methods.

Modjeski's next project was a highway bridge in Portland which also carried two tracks of the urban railway over the Willamette River. The main part of the bridge consists of simple supported truss spans with the roadway at the level of the lower beam. To accommodate river navigation, one of the spans is a double bascule (twin leaf) drawbridge. The total length of this section is 521 feet.

Today, over eighty years after its completion, the bridge continues to carry traffic. Its drawbridge remains one of the three largest raised spans of its type in the world. During this project Modjeski had the opportunity to use his experience from Chicago, a city rich in drawbridges where he had lived for many years. It would be difficult to find a city on earth which has more drawbridges than Chicago. In 1903, he had been a technical consultant to the city and came into contact with the problems of drawbridges on almost a daily basis.

In 1912, Modjeski received a commission to construct a bridge across the Maumee River in Toledo, Ohio, the Cherry Street Highway Bridge. This project was the first in a series of reinforced concrete bridges designed and built under his supervision.

Immediately after the completion of these projects, he designed and supervised the construction of two new bridges over the Mississippi, the fourth and fifth bridges that he built over North America's largest river. These were the two track Harahan Railroad Bridge in Memphis, Tennessee, and a two-level road and railway bridge at Keokuk, Iowa, near the mouth of the Des Moines River.

The Harahan Bridge is situated only about 100 feet from the bridge on which Modjeski worked for Morison. It consists of four great truss spans using the cantilever layout, while one span (on the western side) is reversed and carries the tracks on its upper chord. The main span measures 240 meters (787 feet), and the full length of the bridge, including approaches, is 1.5 kilometers or nearly a mile. The bridge is somewhat lost among its neighbors, for in 1950 an additional highway bridge was built alongside by the Modjeski and Masters engineering company. The trio of bridges contain a total mass of steel found nowhere else. Standing alone Modjeski's Harahan Bridge might be regarded as one of the largest bridges in America. Despite its age, it fulfills its original function well and there has even been discussion about abandoning Morison's bridge and routing all rail traffic across the Harahan Bridge, which could easily accommodate the additional load.

Bridge building was Modjeski's profession, but his interests and talents were many. In 1916, he accepted an appointment to a three-man commission organized by the Public Service Corporation of New Jersey to study the possibility of constructing a tunnel under the Hudson River, and wrote a preliminary study of such an undertaking. He also was a consultant on a two-track railway bridge over the Ohio River at Metropolis, Illinois. At first, he worked with C. H. Cartlig, but after that engineer became ill, he took over the project as chief engineer and completed the work within two years. The load-carrying configuration of this bridge consists of six simple supported truss spans each 720 feet long with curved upper chords. For nearly half a century, these would remain the longest simple supported spans in the world. (This record was topped in 1974 when a span of 822 feet was completed at Chester, Pennsylvania.)

The large spans were constructed of various steel alloys. Members subjected to the highest loads were made out of nickel alloy steel; while the remaining members were made from less expensive but nearly as durable silicon steel. The Metropolis bridge was the first in which silicon steel was used in such great quantities. While not as strong as nickel steel, the quality of the formed steel shapes is higher because it is easier to form on rolling mills. It is also easier to drill for riveted joints. The spans running above the shallows are shorter, and in his customary way Modjeski constructed them as trusses with the roadway supported by the upper chord. The total length of the bridge is nearly two kilometers (one and a quarter miles). (Later, working for the government of the United States, Modjeski built a bridge across the Tanana River, a tributary of the Yukon River, near Fairbanks, Alaska, where the main span was nearly as long—700 feet.)

The bridge at Metropolis opened in 1917, a good year for bridges in America. In that year, four imposing bridges entered into the history of bridge building. Gustav Lindenthal finished the mighty Hell Gate Bridge over the East River in New York and the Sciotoville Bridge over the Ohio River. (On completion, Hell Gate became the world's largest arch bridge[5] while the Sciotoville Bridge was the largest example of a twin-span continuous truss bridge for a quarter century, and became the archetype for bridges of this type in America.) In the same time period Modjeski finished two bridges, one at Metropolis, and the other across the St. Lawrence River near Quebec, which will be discussed later.

Such were the times, the country, the people. As engineers pushed existing limits, record setting became the norm.

Ralph Modjeski in 1914.

During these years, Modjeski and his staff designed and built a smaller yet technically challenging railroad bridge over the Thames River at New London, Connecticut, and completed the rebuilding of a bridge across the Hudson River at Poughkeepsie, New York, for the Central New England Railway Company. The load-bearing portion of the Thames bridge consisted of simple supported trusses, with the center span a massive single bascule drawbridge to allow for the passage of river craft. Such constructions, even today, present many of technical problems not only from the structural aspect but from the mechanical as well. Modjeski's talent, linked with a deep theoretical understanding of the subject, allowed him to create solutions that are still emulated today. During his career, he created a number of moveable bridges—vertical lift, bascule, and rotary. In each case, his solution took into account the conditions at the site and the navigational needs of the waterway.

The enormous railroad bridge across the Firth of Forth in Scotland, completed in 1890 by Sir Benjamin Baker still held the record for the length of its main span 512 meters (1,680 feet). The record held for twenty-seven years.

But it was only a matter of time for someone to top this record in America. The task was placed into the hands of Theodore Cooper, formerly assistant to James Eads during the building of the Mississippi Bridge at St. Louis, later one of America's best

The first Quebec Bridge during construction; arrow points out the place where the support failed.

known engineers. In 1904, he began the construction of a great bridge across the St. Lawrence River seven miles west of the city of Quebec, Canada. At this point the channel narrowed and the banks were of a height that would permit the bridge to have a clearance of 150 feet above the water level, necessary for the passage of ocean-going vessels. The construction was to be similar to the Firth of Forth Bridge, but the span was to be greater.

It is difficult to imagine an engineer better prepared than Cooper to undertake this extremely difficult task. He was a well known and recognized authority, his experience was long-ranging, he had published a series of books,[6] and he created universally used standards. But in designing the bridge, Cooper worked under difficult conditions, constantly under pressure to decrease costs by keeping to a minimum the amount of steel used, while, despite the enormity of the project, there were no resources for conducting tests.

Despite the unfavorable circumstances, construction proceeded, but the first attempt to span the distance of 1,800 feet (549 meters) ended in tragedy. On August 29, 1907 the entire south side of the main structure and four sections of the sus-

pended center span crashed into the river. In several seconds, twenty thousand tons of steel bridgework were no longer standing. Of the eighty-nine workers on the bridge, only eleven survived. Aside from the collapse of a bridge across the Firth of Tay, in Scotland in 1879, this is the greatest disaster in the annals of bridge building.

It was also a personal tragedy for Cooper, who despite his age was at the pinnacle of his creative powers and professional fame. A strong and reliable engineer in one day became ruined. He never recovered. Twelve years later, in 1919, he died, still a broken man.

Each great bridge is an attempt to push the known boundaries. It also presents new problems that must be solved without time-tested solutions. The engineering professional who builds such bridges must be able to face certain hazards. These sometimes force him to make decisions on which he stakes his entire career. And success is never assured. Cooper experienced this personally.

After the catastrophe, the Canadian government conducted an investigation and named a three-man international engineering commission to examine the causes of the accident, redesign the bridge, and supervise the construction of a new structure from start to finish. Almost a year after the disaster, the commission convened at the Dominion Ministry of Railroads and Canals in Ottawa. It was composed of H. E. Vautelet (Canada), Ralph Modjeski (United States), and Maurice F. Fitzmaurice (England). (In a later interview, Modjeski joked that the Canadian was actually a Frenchman, the Englishman was a Scot, and the American a Pole.) Modjeski's appointment to this commission as the engineering representative from the United States testifies to the high esteem and respect that he had gained on the basis of his professional work in his new homeland.

The direct cause of the Quebec disaster was the buckling of the lower chord of the truss in the vicinity of the south pillar. The chord that had given way was insufficiently braced, with cross sections of bracing elements insufficient in comparison to the beams they were to brace. The accident thus became an incentive for various scientific centers to conduct studies of deformation in steel elements, and led to a better understanding and application of Euler's theory of deformation. The commission also found a number of errors in the original design including imprecise calculation of loading and too high a level of allowed stress. As happens after such accidents, careful examination also found errors in the way assembly had been conducted.

After the investigation a number of basic changes were recommended: revisions to the dimensions including the length of the main span and the cross section of load bearing elements; the use of nickel alloy steel with a 40 percent higher strength rating; and an increase from 67 to 87 feet in the height of the chord over the supports.

During the analysis extensive experiments were conducted, and the results applied to a new bridge design. The experiments included tests of the stability of elements made from alloy steels. Modjeski also conducted experiments with the use of nickel steel rivets in joining metal members. These tests did not yield good results and the new bridge was built using conventional steel rivets. (Over 3 million rivets were used on this particular bridge.)

Reconstruction of the Quebec Bridge was carried out by a government Board of Engineers, with Modjeski as a member. In response to the 1907 disaster a far more massive bridge was created. In the case of the lower chord, this is well portrayed by the drawings above. (For comparison purposes, the cross section of the corresponding beam in the Firth

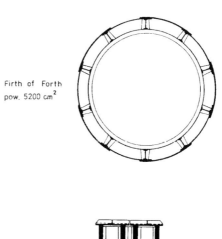

Firth of Forth
pow. 5200 cm^2

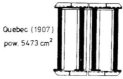

Quebec (1907)
pow. 5473 cm^2

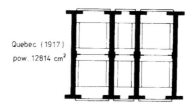

Quebec (1917)
pow. 12814 cm^2

Comparison of the lower chord cross sections of the Firth of Forth, first and second Quebec bridges.

of Forth bridge is included.) The overall weight of steel in the Quebec Bridge in the new design (on the basis of weight per unit of length) was more than twice that of the Firth of Forth Bridge. The increased dimensions were due to greater load requirements of the Quebec Bridge, for in the twenty years that had passed since the Firth of Forth Bridge was built the weights of locomotives and trains had increased considerably, as had the frequency of rail traffic.

Each of these structures, still the world's largest cantilever bridges, was designed in the special atmosphere generated by disaster. Construction of the Firth of Forth Bridge began just four years after the Firth of Tay tragedy near Dundee, Scotland[7] when the multispan bridge fell during a stormy December night, taking 13 spans and the unlucky passengers of a train into the dark waters. It was necessary to have a special kind of courage and faith in one's knowledge not to fall under the

Wreckage of the first Quebec Bridge after the disaster of August 29, 1907.

The engineering commission for the new Quebec Bridge. Standing inside a portion of the lower chord manufactured for the replacement bridge are: (from left) Ralph Modjeski, C. N. Monsarrat, and C. C. Schneider. Photograph courtesy of Modjeski and Masters, Inc.

A fast thinking photographer captured the fall of the center span during the construction of the second Quebec Bridge.

depressing effect of such a disaster. Such courage was shown by both Benjamin Baker in the case of the Firth of Forth Bridge and Ralph Modjeski at Quebec.

In 1910 the St. Lawrence Bridge Company Ltd.-Montreal was created, and a year later work began on the bridge under the constant supervision of Ralph Modjeski, the most active member of the supervisory commission. By 1916, side spans were in place and the cantilevers began to move out over the channel. This bridge differed from the Firth of Forth Bridge in that a more modern method was utilized during assembly. To limit the amount of work done on-site, large prefabricated parts of the bridge were assembled at the shops and transported to the construction site. This technique was reflected in the static stress calculations. Not only were stresses for use and assembly calculated, transport stresses were taken into account as well. Thanks to other improvements in the technologies utilized, 67 thousand tons of steel were assembled in less than three years. This record stood firm for twenty years until the building of the Oakland Bay Bridge in California.

In September of 1916, work began to raise the center span, assembled on shore and floated into position on barges. It was 640 feet long and weighed 4,710 tons making it one of the ten largest simple supported spans in the world. Lifting proceeded simultaneously on four corners, winches having been installed at the ends of the extended cantilevers. As the span was reaching its final position, there was a shift in the load and the southeastern lift point failed so that the steel framework that had just been raised twisted and fell into the river. Thirteen workers died; the same number were injured. Thanks to the exceptional quickness of a photographer who captured the event, we have a unique photograph of the bridge span at the moment of its destruction. It was later determined that the failure of the lift point was due to flaws in the steel.

The catastrophe put Modjeski's abilities to the test. He went through some difficult moments but in the end was completely vindicated. Within a year, a new span was built without significant changes and assembly continued. Lifting the new assembly into position was a four-day operation and was crowned with complete success.

By December 1917, the bridge was essentially finished. Railway tracks were put into operation as the final construction tasks were being completed. This largest of all cantilever bridges was completed in mid-1918.

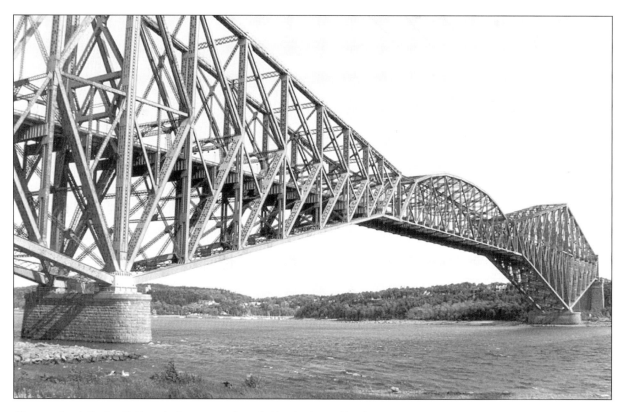

The completed Quebec Bridge, the largest cantilever bridge in the world. Photograph courtesy of Modjeski and Masters, Inc.

The example of this bridge shows us the price of progress in bridge building. The span of Quebec Bridge is 1,800 feet long, exceeding the Firth of Forth Bridge by 100 feet. The extra 100 feet were purchased at the cost of two great disasters and the lives of 91 men.[8]

During the ten years that the Engineering Commission for the Quebec Bridge was active, its membership had changed. The first to leave, in 1910, was Maurice Fitzmaurice. The departure of this excellent British engineer, who worked on the Firth of Forth Bridge with Benjamin Baker, increased the responsibilities and duties placed on Modjeski. In time, he became the person making the crucial technical decisions. He was the only member of the commission to work on it for the full ten years and

it was he who signed the final report. A photograph from the official ceremonies at the opening of the bridge on August 22, 1919, shows the four most important figures at the center of the ceremonies: the Duke of York (later King George VI) who had the honor of cutting the ribbon; the Governor-General of Canada; the Canadian Minister of Railroads and Canals; and Ralph Modjeski.

The design and completion of the bridge were the direct result of Modjeski's effort and perseverance, and he was rewarded with worldwide fame. His work in Canada put him among the top engineers of that country and was a worthy continuation of the work of another famous Pole, Kazimierz Gzowski, who built the first railroads and great bridges there.

Chapter 5

Within the Family

One of his longtime friends once wrote of Ralph Modjeski's character traits:

> To understand him, one must consider the fact that he inherited an artist's temperament. It was not a temperament of the type that is used to justify irrational behavior, but a delicate perception that assures a balance of good taste and harmony in the work at hand, whether it is music, architecture, art, or engineering.

In his appearance he was rather slender and in height just above average. When he gained weight in later life he was never overweight. Imitating his father's style he wore a moustache and beard. His balding head made him seem older than his years.

This talented engineer was a quiet controlled man in his daily life. He never raised his voice or showed anger or agitation. He was economical in his movements, very British in his behavior, using no unnecessary hand gestures. "There was something theatrical in him," said Ignacy Morawski who knew him well.

One of Ralph Modjeski's character traits was reserve, rather than ebullience. He did not seem to form close friendships. As an employer he paid well but was demanding, expecting full responsibility and precision from his staff in their work. He thought that in his profession these were determining factors. He was devoted to the work and did not count the hours, and expected the same dedication from his employees. He demanded mobility—necessary when one considers the responsibilities and distribution of the projects under construction.

His abilities in staff selection were superb; he was used to dealing with people and that made for a well functioning team. Because of his constancy and evenhandedness, and also a modesty in dealing with those around him, he had the full respect of those in his circle. Perhaps this was due to the fact that he was not driven by money. His mother did not leave him a large estate, perhaps 120 to 150 thousand dollars. In the last quarter of his life his earnings were large, yet this did not hold much meaning for him. He lived well, as had his mother. But to him the realization of an idea was the driving force in his activities more important than the money involved.

From 1893, when he established his own engineering design office, he worked with many other engineers. In the first years of the twentieth century he was partner to Alfred Noble. During the building of the McKinley Bridge and after, he worked closely with F. E. Washburn director of works, or resident engineer, in St. Louis. In 1910, after Modjeski acquired some renown, a young engineer from Nebraska, Clement Edwards Chase, graduate of Cornell University, joined his firm. In the 1920s Frank Masters became a close co-worker.

After Chase's tragic death in 1930, when he fell while inspecting the Philadelphia-Camden Bridge, another young engineer Montgomery B. Case, came into the firm. Chase, Masters, and Case began as employees in the design office, then advanced to became partners. It is illustrative of Modjeski's character that he was always interested in advancing young people and including them in his professional family.

As head of a company he was of necessity a sharp observer with unconstrained horizons, always on the pulse of technological progress. He knew the realities of business: how to evaluate the possibilities inherent in each project and how to fight for his ideas. He was always eager to enlarge his contacts with the professional world, and did not hesitate to invite collaboration by experts in

Helena Modjeska, later in her career. Photograph courtesy of Halka Chronic.

related fields in order to solve specific technical or scientific problems. During the 1930s he maintained contact with Daniel E. Moran, a leading expert on soil mechanics and foundation design. Another contact was the architect Paul P. Cret. In the building of his projects he worked with several outstanding engineers of the time: Walter E. Engler, Glen Woodrow, and George H. Randal. For several years in Modjeski's firm the chief draftsman, before he left to form his own company, was Joseph Baerman Strauss, who went on to build the Golden Gate Bridge in San Francisco.

Modjeski's involvement in professional activity by no means exhausted his capabilities. The breadth of his interests is reflected in his social activities. He was never an engineer who existed enclosed in the shell of his own specialization. He found time and energy to be active in scientific and professional associations not only in the United States, but in Canada, Great Britain, and France. The list of these groups is impressive; it includes twenty-one organizations, in some of them he reached the highest ranks. In the most important civil engineering organization in the United States, the American Society of Civil Engineers he was a board member for many years. He was also a board member of the American Institute of Consulting Engineers (AICE) and the New York State Society of Professional Engineers and Land Surveyors. He became an honorary member of the Franklin Institute of the State of Pennsylvania and the Princeton Engineering Association, and maintained a lifelong membership in the Western Society of Engineers. In 1903 he was chosen as president of the Midwest section of this large organization and later was made an honorary member. When he moved to New York, he maintained his link with the organization. Wide-ranging contacts with professional organizations, while motivated by ideals, were also necessary for the ordinary conduct of day-to-day business. Modjeski understood that his professional opportunities and those of his engineering company depended to a large measure on his standing in professional associations and the personal contacts he was able to maintain in this sphere.

At this time Modjeski considered himself to be the premier American bridge builder, which he quite probably was. He was part of America, and able to move through all the compartments of the world he inhabited. His office was located, not by chance, at 28 East Jackson Boulevard, just a few steps away from the Chicago Board of Trade, still one of the world's great financial institutions. In his time, the important financial markets were in London, Paris, New York, and Chicago, with Chicago the most flexible and innovative. Modjeski understood the close relationship between the financial and construction industries. He knew how to utilize the link that bound these two business areas together.

Knowing Modjeski's family history and his artistic abilities, it is not surprising that he was also an active member in various cultural societies. Among these he was involved in activities of the Chicago Art Institute and on the board at the Metropolitan Museum of Art in New York. He belonged to several clubs and societies, among them: the Quadrangle Club, the Union League, Tau

Beta Pi, and Homewood, all prominent in the industrial and cultural life of the Midwest. He was also one of the founders and a long time president of the Engineers Club. Membership in the American Philosophical Society and the Association for the Advancement of Science also say much about his disciplined yet colorful personality.

He had a deeply imbedded sense of fairness, not in the sense of the so-called social justice, but in general. He contributed to charitable causes, quietly and without ostentation. He was sensitive to others, but often found it difficult to express his feelings or give words of praise.

In describing the life and activities of Ralph Modjeski it would be impossible to omit his family life. In his family, internal relationships were extremely complicated and yet were very close. Contact between family members was valued and maintained even when some effort was necessary to do so.

His mother was a person whose motivations were a desire for fame and a love for her family. She took an interest in those who fell into her sphere of influence and tried to assist them. In time, thanks to her help, twenty members (including the second generation) of her family came to the United States.

Raised by a loving mother, Ralph was devoted to her to the end of her life. In one matter, however, they were not of one mind. As soon as Ralph reached his majority he reestablished contact with his father, met with him repeatedly, and helped him materially. It would be difficult to imagine that the two would not have met during Ralph's stay in Europe. When as a wedding present from his mother he received the Modrzejów estate in Zakopane, he made his father its caretaker. And it is impossible that the wedding of Helena Zimajer, his half-sister could have been staged at Modrzejów without his knowledge. But little is known about the contacts between father and son during the final years of the nineteenth century. Gustav Zimajer died in Warsaw on May 3, 1901.

Ralph's personal family life started off well. His mother wrote in a letter dated near the end of 1896 from her Arden estate in California that "the family is doing well, though Felicie suffers from the nerves."

The "nerves" may have been due to suspicions, either the imaginings of an emotional person or real accusations against a hard-working husband who was rarely at home. Whatever the reason, the

Ralph Modjeski, photograph taken in 1917. Photograph courtesy of Halka Chronic.

internal situation in Ralph and Felicie's marriage was visibly deteriorating.

As misunderstandings increased a destructive factor may have been Felicie's attitude, influenced greatly by the fact that she had to live in an environment that was foreign to her. She never liked America and was only comfortable in her familiar places. She liked the atmosphere of visits and receptions among the so called "good families" of Galicia. Thanks to her mother-in-law (also her aunt) no door in Poland was closed to her. She maintained contacts with artistic circles (Józef Chełmoński and Leon Wyczółkowski). For Helena Modrzejewska, during her early days in Kraków, it had been a kind of success to have an audience at the Potocki palace. Felicie was able to call there as a matter of course.

How could a marriage between two such different people endure? On the one hand Ralph quickly adjusted to America and felt at home there. On the other hand Felicie considered America a foreign land. He was an industrious, hard working, self-made man, an American; she a woman who never had to support herself and whose mind was still under the influence of the atmosphere that emanated from the homes of the Galician nobility. Ralph's work required that he give it all his attention for weeks at a time; Felicie was left with the children during those absences.

In the summer of 1902 Felicie took the children to Europe. She spent time in Kraków and wintered in Zakopane. Ralph at this time was fully occupied in building the bridge over the Mississippi at Thebes.

In October of that year Helena Modjeska wrote to her friend Anna Wolska from the Chłapowski estate in Żegocina, Poland, "In the spring we will return to America, Felicie and the children are coming with us, as they are spending the winter in Zakopane. Poor Ralph is alone in Chicago with only work for company." There is a photo of Marylka, Ralph's daughter, with her grandmother on a train platform at the Zakopane railroad station accompanied by Polish writer Stanisław Witkiewicz.

Yet the Chłapowskis returned to America before Felicie and the children. In June 1903 Helena wrote from Chicago to Anna Chłapowska, "We are staying at Ralph's, who as always is very attentive to me and satisfies my smallest needs. It is pleasant and good to be with him. There is a servant who comes in to cook and clean so I don't even have to leave the house." This was probably the first time in a long while that Ralph and his mother were together without Felicie.

For several years Ralph had rented a spacious apartment on the seventeenth floor of the Monadnock Building, with a view of Lake Michigan. Later, he moved three blocks to a luxury apartment at 504 Washington Avenue.

There were many good days there and evenings, when friends gathered at the apartment, many artists among the guests. The Modjeskis were hosts to the famous pianist Josef Hoffman (the son of Kazimierz, Ralph's piano teacher in Kraków). There went Anton Rubinstein and his nearly forgotten brother Nicholas, also a talented pianist, and the lesser known Zofia Menter and Elenora Bloomfield-Zeisler. Among the Polish guests was the famous operatic singer Marcella Sembrich, long a friend of Helena Modjeska. Though Ralph was three years her junior she considered him a friend and was a frequent guest in his house.[1] Often there were visits by other family members, notably Władysław Benda, a recognized painter, mask-maker, and graphic artist, and Wojciech Morawski, a writer and activist, then an editor for Polish-American publications.

In a word it was a glittering American-European household. Those who visited the Modjeskis made their living in America, but brought an intangible inheritance from Europe.

When Ignacy Paderewski was in Chicago, he became the star of the evening. This future Prime Minister of the Polish Republic was a presentable man, a brilliant personality and even without his fame as a pianist, would become the center of interest in any gathering. Ralph had much in common with him: their climbs to the top of their respective professions, their illustrious careers and the accompanying financial rewards. Paderewski, from each of his tours, earned not only the admiration of his audiences, but, as the press estimated, between 100 and 200 thousand dollars. Modjeski matched this income on each of his large bridges. Each followed his own path but ran along a similar course. Thus there was reason for interesting conversations around the holiday table, as in 1905 when Paderewski spent Christmas at the Modjeskis. Modjeska, Sembrich, Hoffman, Paderewski—one must admit that it was a sterling group for any home!

Modjeska and her husband visited Chicago much more often than Ralph visited California, but his family gladly spent time at their grandmother's Arden estate. In 1887 the Chłapowskis had built a beautiful house in the still wild part of Santiago Canyon, where many years previously the young Ralph made exploratory trips. The circle closed, Helena had returned to the place where she first began her life in America, less than 20 miles from Anaheim, California.

The home was designed by famous architect Stanford White. The small estate was named Arden by the actress who reached into Shakespeare for inspiration. The little community of Modjeska lies nearby today, and the estate is part of an Orange County Park. The California property was used for entertaining, but also served to fill the need of possessing land, a need common both to the Kraków city branch of the family and those who were from the farmlands of Poland.

In the years 1903–1906, when Modjeski was working on bridges in Oregon he came to Arden several times. His children also visited there. The grandmother spared them neither attention nor good will and usually conversed with them only in Polish.

In the summer of 1906 Helena Modjeska moved to an apartment in Santa Barbara (Arden was sold), and celebrated the occasion with a reception for eighty guests. It was an appropriate occasion: her grandson Felix had reached his nineteenth birthday. Immediately after this family affair Ralph went to Europe to get his wife and his youngest son Karolek. He spent some time in Kraków but then stopped in England to visit, his daughter Marylka then attending the same convent school which her mother had attended twenty years before.

In the next year, Ralph's entire family traveled to Europe, spending the summer in Brittany, France. At the end of 1907 Ralph returned to California and spent over a week with his mother. From a letter written to her granddaughter we can see that Modjeska was affected by this visit.

Granddaughter Marylka was always a favorite. In 1908 Helena wrote about her with pride in a letter from Bay Island. "My granddaughter Marylka is sixteen. She passed the entrance exam for Oxford and plays the piano beautifully. … They, that is my son, daughter-in-law, Marylka, and Karolek—the youngest grandchild—are going to Zakopane for a few weeks."

Ralph and family were in Kraków in 1909, but for a different purpose. On the afternoon of July 17 Ralph accompanied his mother's casket from the Church of the Holy Cross to the Rackowicki Cemetery.

The *Tygodnik Illustrowany* [Illustrated Weekly] in Kraków printed photographs from the funeral. One of these shows Ludwik Solski, then director of the Kraków theatre, who delivered the eulogy. Karol Chłapowski, Ralph Modjeski, Felicie, Marylka and Felix are pictured as well. It is one of the last photographs of the Modjeski family.

Market Street Bridge in Harrisburg, Pennsylvania as it is today.

8174. Douglas Street Bridge and Water Front, Omaha, Nebr.

Douglas Street Bridge in Omaha, Nebraska, contemporary postcard.

Chapter 6

A String of Successes

The period of Modjeski's most intense activity as an engineer came during the 1920s. The projects he built during this time enlarged his reputation in the engineering community of the United States where he was now a member of an elite group of leading bridge builders that included James Eads, John and Washington Roebling, George Morison, Theodore Cooper, Gustav Lindenthal, Leon Moisseiff, Joseph Baerman Strauss, David Steinman and Othmar Ammann.

During the years 1920–1930 Modjeski and his firm completed nearly twenty great bridges, certainly an impressive figure. He played a leading role in each project, both in design and construction. Several were large bridges over major rivers: the Missouri, Ohio, and Delaware. He was over sixty years old at that time.

During the years 1920 to 1922 he worked on rebuilding two large bridges: a two track railroad bridge over the Ohio River in Cincinnati, and a highway and tramline bridge over the Missouri at Omaha (the Douglas Street Bridge). Reconstruction work proceeded without interruption to traffic, and without scaffolding on the river.

Thirty years had passed since he had been in the city where he started his professional career. Those who work in engineering understand the sentiment that binds them to their first project and the reflections that it brings years later. But Modjeski did not have much time for reminiscing. Despite his age he was still one of the most active engineers in the United States. In addition he was not limited to a narrow field.

His main interest was in building steel bridges, but he was at ease with reinforced concrete. The arch bridge he constructed during 1912-1915 in Toledo was not his only bridge of this type. Ten years later, with Frank Masters, he designed and erected two large bridges over the Susquehanna River at Harrisburg, the state capital of Pennsylvania. Clarks Ferry Bridge, the first of the two, had fifteen reinforced concrete arches, each with a 140-foot span. By current standards these are not large spans but the overall design is very modern and esthetically balanced. The arches are flattened, the piers are slender, and the open construction of the arches with spandrels—not widely used at the time—speak well of the designer. The second, Market Street Bridge, is a four lane highway bridge of more conventional design. The solid arches are faced with stone. It is a long structure, totaling 3,611 feet.

During this phase of his career, Modjeski built many bridges in the eastern part of the United States. In the 1920s he moved his headquarters from Chicago to New York City, locating his offices in Manhattan at 38th Street, with an apartment on Park Avenue. His choice of these addresses indicated not only his relative wealth and social position, but also that his firm was an efficiently functioning and prospering organization. The increase in business soon led to the opening of branch offices in Harrisburg, Philadelphia and New Orleans.

Near the beginning of his independent career, during the design of the bridge at Thebes, Modjeski had met a young metallurgical engineer named Frank M. Masters. During the construction of the bridges at Harrisburg they met again, and Modjeski invited him to join the firm. In 1929 Masters became a partner and the name of the engineering company became Modjeski and Masters. After many years the company, under the same name, continues to build bridges.

By 1920 Ralph Modjeski was already well known as a designer and engineer. But he had not

Clarks Ferry Bridge near Harrisburg, Pennsylvania. This 15 span concrete arch bridge has since been replaced with a new structure resting on the same piers. Photograph courtesy of Modjeski and Masters, Inc.

yet built a suspension bridge. This was to be the final step to fame.

After all he lived in the country where John Roebling and his son Washington had established a reputation on suspension bridges. Three years before Ralph had finished his studies in Paris, the Brooklyn Bridge was opened. At the time it was regarded as the eighth wonder of the world. Its main span was 1,595 feet (486 meters) long, an unheard of length considering the technology of the time. Modjeski may have looked at that bridge with wonder, admiration, and possibly a twinge of envy. In Cincinnati, during the reconstruction of a bridge across the Ohio River he saw the nearby suspension bridge built in 1867 by John Roebling. Its span was 322 meters (1,057 feet), and for thirteen years it was the largest structure of its type in the world. Though cantilever bridges allowed great distances to be spanned, he could see the day when this technology would be surpassed.

Modjeski entered the field of suspension bridge design when he received a contract to build a bridge across the Delaware River to connect Philadelphia, Pennsylvania, and Camden, New Jersey. The project was preceded by a 1920 report authored by a three-man commission (Ralph Modjeski, George S. Webster, and Laurence A. Ball) which analyzed possible ways of crossing the riv-er. Several variations of cantilever and suspension bridges were considered. The suspension bridge was found to be less expensive and easier to build.

In the following year Ralph Modjeski stepped down as chief of the commission in order to devote all his time to the project. The Philadelphia-Camden (now Benjamin Franklin) Bridge was his most important assignment. He was not only chief engineer during construction but also head of the engineering design team. The bridge opened on July 1, 1926, in time for the Sesquicentennial of the Declaration of Independence; at that time it was the largest suspension bridge in the world and the first of the type to be built in a modern, mature form. The length of the main span 533.4 meters (1,750 feet), bested the three large New York bridges across the East River (the Brooklyn, Manhattan, and Williamsburg Bridges) that had set the standard for this type of construction in the United States and the world.

Built at the cost of 36 million dollars, the Benjamin Franklin Bridge distinguishes itself by its graceful, slim silhouette and impressive appearance, effects due to judicious choices in the dimensions of the towers and stiffening truss, and to the construction of the load carrying-cables. The tall 382-foot (110-meter) steel cross-braced towers were used in this form for the first time.

The Philadelphia-Camden (Benjamin Franklin Bridge), sketch by Krzysztof Szymanski. Courtesy of Joseph Zazyczny.

Modjeski was a pioneer in using steel pylons instead of massive stone towers. The deck is suspended from two main cables, each 30 inches (760 millimeters) in diameter, composed of nearly 19 thousand individual wires laid in place during construction. Twenty-five thousand miles of wire, or 3,500 tons of special steel alloy, were used in the cables. The length of the bridge was extraordinary: together with the approaches it was 9,620 feet (1.82 miles or nearly three kilometers) long.

Modjeski's design, as in his bridge at Metropolis, specified steel alloys with special qualities. The pylons were built of silicon steel; the stiffening members, designed in the form of Warren trusses, had upper and lower beams of nickel steel. In the 18 thousand tons of steel in the bridge nearly one-third is nickel steel, more expensive and harder to machine, but stronger and more resistant to corrosion than other alloys in common use.

The foundations were constructed under difficult conditions. The pylons were attached to massive caissons with a footprint of 21 by 43 meters (69 by 141 feet) which were sunk into the river bed to a depth of over 20 meters (66 feet).

During the design phase, Modjeski conducted studies to solve problems which arose during the construction of this pioneering bridge. He organized a research unit in his firm under the leadership of his young co-worker, Clement Chase, which addressed the deflection of stiffening members and durability of the supporting cables.

On the day of its opening Ralph Modjeski became the builder of the longest cantilever bridge (Quebec) and the longest suspension bridge (Philadelphia). At this time Othmar Ammann was already at work designing a new bridge across the Hudson for New York City and in 1931 it would become the boldest undertaking in bridge building, but until that time Modjeski was in the leading position.

On the occasion of the bridge opening, Philadelphia threw a massive public celebration. *The Evening Bulletin* ran a lengthy article on the subject. It is worthwhile to repeat a few fragments, as in it Modjeski is portrayed by a contemporary writer.

The Philadelphia-Camden Bridge during construction.

The Philadelphia-Camden Bridge as it was shortly after its opening. Photograph shows the Camden, New Jersey, entrance.

Ralph Modjeski flanked by New Jersey Governor A. Harry Moore (left) and Pennsylvania Governor Gifford Pinchot (right) during an official inspection of the bridge on March 19, 1926. Photograph courtesy of Modjeski and Masters, Inc.

The Philadelphia-Camden Bridge (now the Benjamin Franklin Bridge) as it is today.

Delaware Bridge opens with a great acclaim, so great that in all the tumult and the shouting little enough of the credit for the big span seems likely to go to the modest man who built it, and regards it as the greatest work of his life of bridgebuilding, the engineer Ralph Modjeski.

A man of medium height who wears his sixty-five years lightly, the grizzled constructor of the Delaware Bridge is a familiar figure to the thousands of men whose hands have wrought its webs of steel, piled up its battlemented towers, and fashioned the roadway that swings at such a dizzy height. They have seen him in fair weather, snapping with his little motion-picture hand-camera the progress of the big job. They have seen him straw-hatted and in tweeds, coolest in a crowd of perspiring and coatless inspecting delegates, on a sweltering August day. They know him in formal attire on formal occasions, and they have seen the keen eyes above the grey imperial under the old sou-wester, as the Big Boss scaled ladders and traveled girders with a dirty slant from the North Atlantic slapping a scud of stinging sleet into his face.

Men get to know the Big Boss on jobs like the Delaware bridge. And when the Big Boss is a man like Ralph Modjeski, men get to like him. Out on the end of the steelwork and in his office at the Widener Building they like Ralph Modjeski as a man. And there is that in his personality which instantly prepossesses those who come in contact with him.

The grasp of the hand is quick, and hearty. The bearing bespeaks that inner confidence born out of sure knowledge, the quiet self-contained modesty of the man of parts. The keen features in their moments of gravity are strikingly statesmanlike. …

There are not many men of his age who go down into the sandpits with the sandhogs and out on the girders with the riveters. But the sandhogs and the riveters on the Delaware Bridge have had a chance to get acquainted with the Big Boss right on the job.

Such opinions about Modjeski were not the individual, anonymous views of the reporter. There is ample testimony to this in a letter sent to Modjeski by the United Commission for the Building of a Bridge over the Delaware at the completion of construction. This letter-certificate[1] is beautifully calligraphed on fine paper and decorated with gold lettering and elaborate initial letters. Its content is as follows.

The Delaware River Bridge Joint Commission

Whereas Dr. Ralph Modjeski[2] has this day tendered his resignation as the active Chief Engineer of the Delaware River Bridge Joint Commission effective October 31st, 1926, explaining that he feels that the work he has prosecuted so vigorously and successfully for six years has reached a stage where such action is possible, the Joint Commission is compelled to accept his decision with reluctance and deep feeling.

But it would not be fair to the people of the states of Pennsylvania and New Jersey who are particularly indebted to this great engineer for the magnificent structure spanning the Delaware to permit this occasion to pass without recognition by this Joint Commission.

Dr. Modjeski has given six years of a most valuable and crowded life to our enterprise. He brought to this project ripe experience supplementing the most complete technical knowledge.

Quiet, unassuming, a scholarly engineer and a gentleman in the most exact sense of that word, he took the responsibility for solving the engineering problems that inevitably beset the designing and building of the world's greatest suspension bridge.

His most becoming diffidence and ceremonious courtesy endeared him to every member of the Joint Commission; his absolute knowledge, his wise foresight and the tremendous force he radiated in his accomplishments won the confidence and deepest respect of all who came in contact with him.

Problems in connection with the financing of the project; questions of policy as regards the collection of tolls; decisions as to the kind of legislation required; all those and many more were matters which required deep thought and study on the part of this Commission. But when the question was one of bridge engineering, then no past or present member of this commission was anxious or doubtful, because Dr. Modjeski was the Chief Engineer in all that the title implied.

He was the most competent authority to meet each baffling situation as it arose and this was the dazzling triumph of July 1st when the bridge was thrown open to traffic in accordance with the promise he had made five years earlier.

The Joint Commission is mightily indebted to Dr. Modjeski. So is every man, woman and child of the millions who have crossed the bridge within the last four months and so will everyone of the countless millions yet unborn who will profit by the labor of this scholarly Engineer and who must concur in our judgement today that the

Whereas

DR. RALPH MODJESKI

has this day tendered his resignation as the active Chief Engineer of the Delaware River Bridge Joint Commission, effective October 31st, 1926, explaining that he feels that the work he has prosecuted so vigorously and successfully for six years has reached a stage where such action is possible, the Joint Commission is compelled to accept his decision with reluctance and deep feeling.

Page 1 of a calligraphed document acknowledging Ralph Modjeski's contribution to the construction of the bridge that linked Philadelphia and Camden. Courtesy of Ralph Modjeski Pattison.

He was the competent authority to meet each baffling situation as it arose and his was the dazzling triumph of July 1st when the bridge was thrown open to traffic in accordance with the promise he had made more than five years earlier. The Joint Commission is mightily indebted to Dr. Modjeski. So is every man, woman and child of the millions who have crossed the bridge within the last four months and so will everyone of the countless millions yet unborn who will profit by the labor of this scholarly Engineer and who must concur in our judgment today that the work he is now concluding was a task most excellently done.

Page 5 of calligraphed document acknowledging Ralph Modjeski's contribution to the construction of the bridge that linked Philadelphia and Camden. Courtesy of Ralph Modjeski Pattison.

work he is now concluding was a task most excellently done.

The report is signed by the fourteen members of the commission. It can be treated as a beautiful expression of recognition for the work of the Polish immigrant and respect for his character traits.

The Philadelphia-Camden Bridge was a bold undertaking. The width of the deck was over 40 meters (130 feet). Initially, this was seen as "wanton excess" and voices were raised in protest, but these were quickly silenced. Time confirmed the worth of the design choice: in 1931 twelve million vehicles crossed the bridge,[3] and currently about 100,000 vehicles use it daily.

The bridge found favor not only from users but, what is more difficult to attain, in the eyes of experts. Twenty years after the bridge opened the famous English expert Professor Charles Inglis, in a monograph on construction and engineering, described it as a "supremely beautiful" object. Yet in those twenty years many other new bridges were built which were brilliant technological accomplishments, among them the George Washington Bridge in New York and the Golden Gate in San Francisco.

Between 1927 and 1929 Modjeski simultaneously built three bridges great distances apart, a highway bridge over the Delaware River between Tacony, Pennsylvania and Palmyra, New Jersey; a single-track railroad bridge at Melville, Louisiana over the Atchafalaya River, 90 miles from where it empties into the Gulf of Mexico; and a road bridge across the Ohio River (Clark Memorial Municipal Bridge) between Louisville, Kentucky and Jeffersonville, Indiana.

The main part of the Tacony-Palmyra Bridge is a 551 foot span built as a bowstring arch with two hinge points, accompanied by a double bascule drawbridge. Such a combination was first applied here as away to span a wide river while taking into consideration the navigational requirements. The solution was efficient from an engineering standpoint and esthetically elegant. The roadway is suspended from the arch. There are three approach spans on each side of the arch executed as truss work that supports the roadway from below. Total length of the bridge is 3,658 feet. The double bascule drawbridge, on the east side of the arch ranks among the largest drawbridges of this type in the world. When opened its span is 281 feet. There is a unique quality to this drawbridge: when closed it

The Tacony-Palmyra Bridge on the Delaware River provides avial link between Pennsylvania and New Jersey road systems. The double-bascule drawbridge is on the New Jersey side of the archa.

The Ambassador Bridge links Detroit, Michigan and Windsor, Ontario. At its completion it was the longest bridge span in the world. Early postcard.

functions as a three-hinge arch.

At the time the Tacony-Palmyra Bridge opened there already existed a larger arch bridge, the Hell Gate Bridge built fifteen years earlier by Gustav Lindenthal over the East River in New York City. But among arch bridges that utilized a moveable section, Modjeski's construction was the largest.

The load-bearing portion of the railroad bridge at Melville consists of ten spans. Six are large simple supported trusses with curved upper chords; three are trusses that support the tracks from below. In the center is a vertical lift drawbridge. The full length of the bridge from end to end is nearly a kilometer (0.6 mile).

The Clark Memorial Municipal Bridge over the Ohio River is an elegant six-span truss construction 80 feet above high water. The main part of the bridge is 3,470 feet long; its full length (including the approaches) is nearly twice that.

Even as he directed work on these three bridges Modjeski was employed as a consultant, project verifier, and construction supervisor of the Ambassador Bridge being built across the Detroit River between the cities of Detroit, Michigan and Windsor, Ontario. There he worked in close cooperation with the McClintic and Marshall Co. of Pittsburgh and its chief engineer Lewis Taylor. The main span

of this bridge, 1,850 feet (564 meters), was 100 feet longer than the Benjamin Franklin Bridge in Philadelphia. It cost 20 million dollars. Supporting cables were made of steel specially heat treated to improve its strength characteristics.[4] The cables were supported by slender pylons whose construction was not unlike those in Philadelphia; however the hinge points were placed at foundation level. Its deck is joined by stiffening members and placed over 40 meters (130 feet) above high water, allowing large ocean-going vessels to pass through. This long bridge (nearly 1.6 miles, or 2.5 kilometers, in total length) is efficient and functional, but lacks symmetry because the approach spans are not coordinated with the main span. The side spans are not suspended from the main cable, and because the trusses are underneath the deck they appear to be mismatched to the main span. The bridge was built in the style of the time, to be efficient, utilitarian and within budget.

The Ambassador Bridge was sited near the heart of Detroit as it was at that time, near the downtown area and the city's main railway terminal Central Michigan Station. Since that time Detroit has changed greatly, enduring the decline and recovery that has affected many industrial cities. The railroad station stands empty now, but

The Henry Avenue Bridge over the Wissahickon Creek Ravine is a majestic arch that crosses the space in single leap and beautifully blends into the lush landscape of Philadelphia's Fairmount Park.

the bridge endures, carrying thousands of cars daily across the border. At night, lights mounted on the structure outline the main suspension cables.

The Ambassador Bridge was a milestone in civil engineering, for a brief time the longest suspension span anywhere in the world, longer than the world's largest cantilever span at Quebec. It soon became obvious that the longest spans would be in suspension bridges. Three years later the George Washington Bridge would set a new standard with a span exceeding a kilometer (1,068 meters or 3,500 feet). Opening ceremonies for the Ambassador Bridge were elaborate, but Modjeski was not able to attend. He was in Japan at the World Engineering Congress, as representative of engineering associations of the United States.

While the Ambassador Bridge was being built, Modjeski also worked with Daniel E. Moran on design and construction of a bridge across the Hudson River at Poughkeepsie, New York. Somewhat smaller than the previous projects with a particular purity and cleanliness of design, this bridge draws one's attention by its slender towers and balanced silhouette. Its main span is 1,500 feet; together with the approaches its total length is 4,007 feet. It was built in the years 1923–1930. Because of the high banks that border the Hudson River the deck had to be placed high over the river's surface, giving it an especially pleasing slim silhouette. Even today, it is considered one of America's most beautiful bridges.

During the years 1927–1931 Modjeski built two more bridges in Philadelphia, both along Henry Avenue. One is a multi-span viaduct over tracks of the former Reading Railroad Company, the other an arch over the deep ravine of the Wissahickon Creek. Both were contracted by the Department of Public Works of the City of Philadelphia, and executed in direct cooperation with Clement Chase, who had started work at the Modjeski and Masters engineering office as a staff member, and later became a partner in the firm.

With the execution of the bridge over the Wissahickon Creek Modjeski showed that he had mastered not only all-steel construction but reinforced concrete structures as well. This road carrying

The highway bridge at Evansville, Indiana. Photograph courtesy of Modjeski and Masters, Inc.

The bridge over the Tennessee River at Paducah, Kentucky. Photograph courtesy of Modjeski and Masters, Inc.

The Mid-Hudson (Roosevelt) Bridge near Poughkeepsie, New York, is considered to be one of the East Coast's most beautiful bridges. Photograph courtesy of Modjeski and Masters, Inc.

Bridge on the Atchafalaya River near Melville, Louisiana. Photograph courtesy of Modjeski and Masters, Inc.

bridge is a steel-reinforced concrete arch with a 300-foot span, faced with stone. It is considered not only a unique engineering accomplishment but a fine example of esthetic elements coordinated with their surroundings.

Between 1930 and 1934 Modjeski was also employed as a consultant on other companies' projects. At the request of the New York City Council he wrote an expert opinion on the proposed Tri-Borough Bridge over the East River. In addition he worked with Frank Masters on two large bridges crossing the Ohio River at Maysville, Kentucky, and Evansville, Indiana. These were the fourth and fifth bridges which he built on that great river. Not only do their overall lengths differ but so does their construction. The one at Maysville is a highway suspension bridge that takes another step forward in construction technique. The main span is 1,060 feet, significantly shorter than the Ambassador Bridge and its form, both the towers and the stiffening beam, are spartan, deprived of any decorative features. It was built during the period 1929–1930.

The second bridge, at Evansville, is a continuous truss with the roadway running along the lower chord, similar to that at Louisville. Its overall length 5,396 feet is considerable. It took seventeen months to finish this bridge in 1932. The pace at which it was built was good but not imposing—perhaps a sign that the rapid rush which characterized the turn of the century was finally running down.

Frank Masters' participation had become significant in the design of road bridges in Kentucky, and on two tributaries of the Ohio River, the Cumberland River at Smithland and on the nearby Tennessee River near Paducah. The bridge near Paducah was a departure from previous designs. The river was spanned with one large truss span that had a curved upper chord. Approaches were constructed as continuous plate girders. Built over the period of three years and finished in 1931, this bridge, was nearly a kilometer (3,032 feet) long.

Despite his age and the responsibilities connected with his own projects, Modjeski still found the time to be a consultant on a project for a large (7,873 foot) single-track railroad bridge across the Missouri River at St. Charles, near its confluence with the Mississippi, just north of St. Louis. This bridge consists mainly of simple supported trusses with parallel chords, so it is not unlike Modjeski's first bridges. It took six years to build.

The Maysville Bridge on the Ohio River. Photograph courtesy of Jan Plachta.

The last and largest project with which Modjeski's name is connected, where his talents were put to the greatest test, is the San Francisco-Oakland Bay Bridge in California. Studies on the problem of bridging the bay started as early as 1915. But the process was drawn out because San Francisco is located in a seismically active area and memories of the great earthquake of 1906 were still fresh. An entire generation of people who endured the destruction of the city was still alive. However, in 1930 Modjeski's firm received a contract for a bridge design based on his concepts and with him as chairman of a board of consulting engineers. It was a difficult undertaking, and not only as an engineering problem. One had to keep in mind that the bay was considered to be one of the most scenic and attractive places on the planet.

In 1931 Modjeski accepted leadership of the board of engineers. The matter was important and

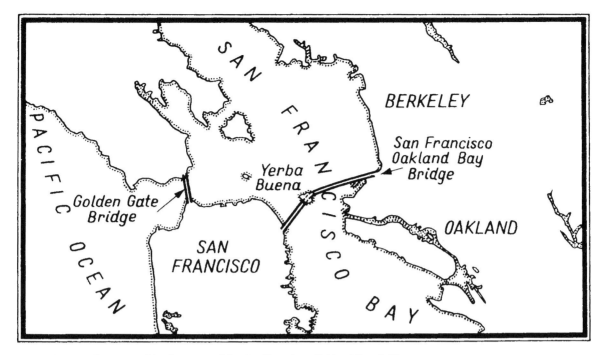

Map showing the geographic placement of the San Francisco-Oakland Bay Bridge.

would not wait. In 1929 ferries transported 39 million passengers and nearly 4.5 million vehicles across the bay. This form of transport had reached its limit. It was necessary to start construction immediately, for time had become an important dimension of all decisions, including the engineering choices.

It was decided that the main, or western part of the bridge would consist of two suspension bridges linked in the center by a massive concrete support that would be the anchor point of the cables from the neighboring spans. The construction of this support (nearly 500 feet tall), which would have to bear enormous loads and rest on bedrock 240 feet below the surface of the water, presented its own set of engineering problems. To date it is the deepest underwater foundation ever achieved in bridge building. The "footprint" (92 by 197 feet) of this support is larger than half a football field. Such construction brought with it the many problems connected to sinking a foundation. Modjeski solved these in turn, as he had on previous projects with the help of Daniel Moran, from the well known New York consulting firm of Moran and Proctor.

The main span in each of the two suspension bridges is 2,310 feet (704 meters). The stiffening members, made of steel specially treated to increase its endurance, support two decks. As originally designed the upper deck had a six lane roadway, the lower carried an interurban two-track railway with three additional lanes for truck traffic.[5]

The eastern part of the bridge consists of a cantilevered truss construction with a center span of 1,400 feet (427 meters) today still one of the largest of its type.[6] It is joined on the Oakland end by several truss spans and a causeway. The two parts of the bridge are connected via a 500 foot tunnel cut through the rock of Yerba Buena Island.[7] Of the 23 thousand tons of steel used in this part of the bridge, more than half are various types of alloy steel.

The project was characterized by efficient organization of work and a terrific pace of progress. The United States was beginning to shake off the effects of the Great Depression. On July 9, 1933, the first shovelful of earth on Yerba Buena Island was turned by President Franklin Delano Roosevelt to inaugurate work on what he called the "greatest bridge to be built by man." On November 12, 1936—three years and four months later—the roadways were opened to traffic. The roadway is, in all, 8.25 miles or 13.2 kilometers long. This averages out to a rate of construction amounting to 33 feet or 10 meters of bridge per day— a truly a remarkable pace. Even now, in western Europe, 3 to 4 meters per day is considered an accomplishment.

The suspension bridge portion of the San Francisco-Oakland Bay Bridge.

During construction Modjeski relocated to Los Angeles. The change of climate had a positive effect on his well-being, but not on his advanced age. His level of energy decreased—he was seventy-five years old—and as his influence lessened and the responsibility for directing the work fell more and more on chief engineer C. H. Purcell and Frank Masters.

Even before construction ended, the Bay Bridge was generally acknowledged to be a major technical achievement. For twenty years (until 1956) it remained the longest and most expensive bridge in the world. The total length from the outermost supports, including the tunnel through Yerba Buena Island is 8.25 miles, while the total cost was over 77 million dollars.

Even today, after a half century—during which time the highway systems of the United States and the world grew enormously—the Oakland Bay Bridge remains among the ten longest bridges in the world. On its two decks there is a constant flow of traffic. At night a fluid stream of lights flickers across the bridge.[8] It has become a recognizable landmark associated with the city, and also an inseparable part of what has been called the "American way of life."

The opening ceremonies took on the aura of a folk festival. Several thousand people attended the observance. Fireworks lit up the sky. Governor Frank F. Merian read verses especially prepared for the occasion, while former President Herbert Hoover gave credit to the builders in his speech. "This structure contains all the experience of our industrial civilization ... It is a product of knowledge acquired over the centuries ..."

Immediately after it was opened the bridge received a special award from the American Institute of Steel Construction (AISC).[9] But to some extent the renown and recognition which the bridge achieved in the engineering community was overshadowed by the simultaneous construction of the world's longest single suspension span across the nearby Golden Gate. The Bay Bridge was an engineering project on a scale several times that of the Golden Gate Bridge. The load it was to carry was much greater. But the record breaking distance spanned by the other bridge—4,203 feet or 1,281 meters—created an excitement that could not be denied.

The Golden Gate Bridge was being built by Modjeski's contemporary, friend, and competitor—Joseph B. Strauss. The relationship between the two

S.F.~OAKLAND BAY BRIDGE.~ PLACING COLLAR ON
CABLE FOR HOLDING THE STRINGERS. Piggott Photo

San Francisco-
Oakland
Bay Bridge

Z-2001

SECTION OF CABLE IN FRONT OF
FERRY BLDG.~S.F. Piggott Photo 1062

Contemporary postcards issued during construction and after the completion of the San Francisco-Oakland Bay Bridge.

Construction photo of work progressing on the San Francisco-Oakland Bay Bridge.

most famous bridge builders of the time is best illustrated by Modjeski's lighthearted statement that Strauss' desire to build large structures was a reaction to his slight stature. Strauss was only five feet tall.

In the small and exclusive group of top American bridge builders—full of individualists—there was no lack of interpersonal friction. Modjeski's relationships with Moisseiff and Moran were always friendly. He did not like the much younger Steinman, and the feeling was reciprocated. (Even Meanna Mengle, longtime personal secretary to Modjeski, spoke of Steinman's unfriendliness.) There were many differences between the two brilliant engineers. It was not just a generational difference. In fact Modjeski, whose personality was reserved and aristocratic, had nothing in common with the extremely talented, gregarious, aggressive American who was raised in a totally different cultural environment.

With Gustav Lindenthal it could have been different. Both men were Europeans who had lived under the rule of the same nation. In the schools that both attended in their youth, the portrait of Franz Joseph was prominently displayed. The

places of their birth were only about 200 miles apart, and they were of the same generation, with Lindenthal eleven years Modjeski's senior. But they never found a common ground. Competition between them was fierce, while personal relations were at best proper.

In discussing engineering projects completed by Ralph Modjeski one must include a bridge over the Mississippi just north of New Orleans. To anchor and support a bridge across the river on the loose, swampy delta deposits was a challenging assignment. Technical studies on this problem started in the 1920s, and after finishing the Philadelphia-Camden bridge Modjeski was in a group of engineers ready to take on this project. As was his custom he made a thorough analysis and submitted his bid. Early in January of 1926 he signed a contract for the project to be supervised by his firm, Modjeski, Masters and Case. The cost of the bridge was estimated at 15 million dollars. It was to be the costliest railroad bridge in the United States.

The initial report detailed various methods of spanning such a long distance. Among the alternatives was a long suspension bridge. There is even a

The Huey P. Long Bridge at New Orleans, Louisiana, is a combination road and rail bridge. Photograph courtesy of Modjeski and Masters, Inc.

monograph "Some Brief Remarks on Suspension Bridges" published in 1927 in the *Proceedings of Louisiana Engineering Society.* But in the end, a decision was made to build it using long trusses.

The bridge is very long because of the extensive swamplands on the shores of the river. The setting of foundations was made especially difficult because of the unconsolidated deposits in the Mississippi Delta. Many experts thought it would be impossible to set foundations there. But the problem was solved by Modjeski, working with Moran and Proctor. Using an artificial island made of sand, they were able to place the main support at a depth of nearly 60 meters (197 feet). The plans, finished in 1930, specified a combination highway and railroad bridge over 4.4 miles or 7 kilometers in length, with a deck high above the river's surface to allow for the navigational requirements. In the meetings that led to the approval of this unconventional project by the Department of Defense, Modjeski played an important part, testifying on the basis of his extensive professional experience.

The start of construction was delayed by difficulties in finding funding for such a large project, and Modjeski was not able to take a direct hand in it, as was his usual custom. But the concepts for the underpinnings and the structure were faithfully executed as he had laid out in the plans. Even though he was well into his seventies he came to New Orleans a number of times, and apparently enjoyed the French atmosphere that was so familiar to him. He solved whatever problems arose during construction and looked over the progress of work being done by the American Bridge Company. Finished in 1935, the bridge is the longest of the twenty-nine bridges that up to that time had been erected across the Mississippi. It is a fine example of an excellent engineering solution applied under difficult conditions. Even today it is one of the world's longest railroad bridges.[10] Despite the years that have passed, it serves well. The structure, whose main elements are made of silicon steel, turned out to be very durable. It is called the Huey P. Long Bridge as a memorial to the American ideologue and populist who served as governor of Louisiana and U.S. Senator.

Altogether, there are nearly forty bridges to which Modjeski made significant contributions. But this fact alone tells little of his tremendous input into the development of the science and engineering involved in bridge building, the field to which he dedicated his life.

During the first years of his professional life Modjeski built mainly truss bridges. Most were simple from the standpoint of the statics involved. Later he built more challenging and mathematically more involved continuous trusses.

The explanation for the use of trusses is not difficult. Railroad bridges require stiff members that, from a statics viewpoint, have a simple distribution of forces and are easy to construct. Though other solutions existed at the time, for example the 861 foot-long suspension bridge over the Niagara River built by John Roebling in 1855, Modjeski intuitively knew that this was not the best solution.

The Gerber truss used in the cantilever configuration was introduced into bridge engineering in the 1870s. Appropriate theory and methods of application, as well as the mathematics involved in determining the size of members, must have been part of the lectures—as something quite innovative—at the Ecole des Ponts et Chaussées. Cantilever bridges quickly gained popularity partly because their construction allowed the spans to be constructed without cumbersome scaffolding in the river.

Truss bridges built by Modjeski—as seen by modern eyes—are not particularly handsome. These huge structures are no doubt useful and economical, yet they do not blend well into their environment. Modjeski was not indifferent to the problems of technological advancement and in a balanced manner sought to improve and perfect his designs. Lengths of the simple supported trusses such as those at Metropolis, Ohio, and Tanana, Alaska, as well as cantilever spans such as Quebec reach dimensions that, for their time, were the largest in the world. In the bridges he designed, the truss members displayed a rational and, progressive for their time, regular pattern of cross supports. Often secondary members are used to attain longer spans. He was a brilliant designer of moveable bridges on busy navigable rivers, building many different varieties: swing, vertical lift, and bascule; some were of remarkable proportions. At the same time he was able to compete on an even basis in this field with the largest firms, including the Chicago-based Strauss Engineering Corporation.

In Modjeski's designs there are no attempts to establish formalistic patterns such as employed in Pauli, Schwendler and other truss types. He also built no bridges that have excessive ornamentation or decorative effects like the bridge over the northern Elbe River in Hamburg, where the chords run in a sinusoidal pattern along all the spans, and where bridge entrances are set off by massive, intricately constructed stone towers.

He resolved all his projects as directly as possible, applying his attention to the heart of each problem, on which the undertaking was based. In the designs of other engineers during this time, the load-bearing structure was often hidden by secondary elements: towers, gates, ornaments, and decorative railings. His designs are clean and bare; but utility was dominant. Decisions were based on function and cost. There is no apparent evidence of attempts to save material, a quality in American bridges of that time. Materials were relatively inexpensive. (In Europe, where skilled labor was always less expensive, more care was put into efficient use of materials. It was an incentive for developing theories. At that time, the scientific level in Europe was above that in America.)

Studying Modjeski's bridges built at the end of the nineteenth century we get an impression that he was an engineer who treated his craft exclusively in a utilitarian way, and paid no attention to the esthetic values of a given design. He was not bothered by using widely different structures visibly mismatched in the same bridge. This is readily apparent when one looks at the place where the main bridge spans meet with the approach spans. Often he directly goes from a large span to short spans that form the approach, these being supported on many trellised steel legs. In this aspect Modjeski did not differ from his contemporaries. But as time passed he began to change. He became fascinated with the material and developed an ability for making the most out of it. In this second, later phase of his career, he truly mastered his field. Without interfering with their function he began to build bridges totally unified in form, and impressive for the balance in their proportions. Beginning in 1928, the American Institute of Steel Construction started awarding annual prizes for the most beautiful bridge. Modjeski was the only engineer who received the award three times.

He also built steel arch bridges. Among the ones most worthy of attention is the bridge across Crooked River canyon. For 1912 the 340 foot (104 meter) span was quite an achievement.

Plate girders are not used frequently in his structures but he does not shy away from them. In the Tennessee River bridge at Paducah, approach spans on both sides of the large truss span are built of continuous-plate girders.

The growth of the rail network in the United States reached a plateau in 1916. In the years that followed the network was rebuilt and upgraded, and some inefficient routes eliminated. The total length of all the rail lines, 250 thousand miles, underwent reduction over the next twenty years at about one percent per year.

Soon the needs of the growing highway network manifested themselves. After all, these were times when Henry Ford flooded America with Model Ts. In 1900 there were eight thousand cars in the United States; two years later over a million were on the roads. By 1915 there were 2.5 million and this was just the beginning. There was no exaggeration in the phrase "Henry Ford put the nation on wheels." Over the next quarter-century thirty million automobiles were produced.

Under these circumstances the building of highways became of major importance, affecting, of course, Modjeski's professional activities. While the first ten of his bridges all carry railroads, of his last ten only three have tracks, and one of these is a combination rail and highway bridge. The situation set the requirements.

In the last ten years of his career (1926–1937) Ralph Modjeski built five suspension bridges, all exceptional structures. At the time of its completion in 1926 the Philadelphia-Camden bridge was the world's largest suspension bridge. Three years later the Ambassador Bridge in Detroit, Michigan, proved that suspension bridges could span greater distances than other types. The Oakland Bay Bridge (1937) became the longest and most heavily used bridge in the world.

But Ralph Modjeski's contribution to bridge building was not limited to creating new records. He was among the first to introduce steel towers (pylons) in place of massive masonry towers. In his designs the towers were of a simple clean construction, as can be seen by comparing the towers of the Ambassador Bridge in Detroit with those of the George Washington Bridge in New York. He also used better grades of steel and unified cables, which gave bridge silhouettes a lightweight appearance.

Switching from heavy stone towers to cross braced steel construction was not merely a change in materials, but testifies to the understanding of the static forces at work in a suspension bridge. His approach was one which took into consideration the fact that all elements were part of a larger whole. Today this is what we call a "systems approach."

Instead of heavy, complicated bearings located on top of the pylons, he used a nearly direct support for the weight-carrying cables. Whereas cables and towers were formerly treated as separate, now they were a unit, with movements at the top compensated for through a flexible design of the support.

His accomplishments left no doubt that he was one of the leading builders of suspension bridges, a worthy successor to Telford and Roebling, a worthy competitor to Strauss. In the years that followed he graciously passed the mantle of leadership to Steinman and Ammann.

But this able master builder did not limit himself to steel structures as shown by his achievements in concrete bridge design. There is the example of his use of concrete in approach spans of the bridge over the Mississippi at Thebes during the years 1902–1905, only ten years after the first concrete-reinforced railroad bridge (only 2.4 meters long) was put into use in Switzerland. Other massive bridges constructed by Modjeski demonstrate the influence of the French school which for over three hundred years led the world in the field. They testify to his excellent command of both stone and concrete as should be expected from a graduate of the Ecole des Ponts and Chaussées.

Modjeski's engineering achievements, his accomplishments in building bridges brought him fame and success. His name is among those of Poles who have made significant contributions to building America's greatness—a signal honor belonging to only a few from among the millions of immigrants.

But such a listing of accomplishments, despite the many facts, is in a sense incomplete—for it does not list the trials and difficulties he had to face. To put it in a few words, the road he traveled was in no way smooth. There were moments when he had to make difficult choices.

In 1909, the year of his mother's death, Ralph was involved in challenging but prestigious engineering projects. He was working intensively. He was building a bridge over the Mississippi at St. Louis, and serving as a member of the Quebec Bridge Commission. At the same time he was preparing a new design for the Quebec Bridge and was employed as a consultant in verifying the Manhattan Bridge project whose construction was already underway. During his involvement in these matters he received word of his mother's illness. He immediately traveled from Montreal to Bay Island, California, and was with her in her last moments. After that he was present at requiem observances in Los Angeles. He ordered the coffin taken to Chicago, where it was placed in a church crypt. Then, for several months he tended to his work. In late June he took the coffin to New York. After an elaborate funeral service at St. Patrick's Cathedral, Cardinal Farley saw the coffin off at the Hoboken docks as it set sail for Poland. (Eighteen English language dailies in New York ran front page stories.) Ralph, however, was not there. He sent a long telegram with instructions to relatives in Poland—Wojciech and Ignacy Morawski and Władysław Benda. Then, as soon as he could get away, he sailed for Europe on the next fast ship reaching Kraków on the day of the funeral.

Any judgement as to his choices between family duty and professional obligations must be left to the opinion of the individual reader. These opinions will no doubt vary, as they did at the time these events took place.

Chapter 7

In the Setting Sun

One may ask about the personal life of the great engineer as he entered the later phase of his life. Over the years his personality did not change much. He was still a hardy man, self-controlled, quiet, gentlemanly, precise in his actions—a person who knew what he wanted. He radiated decisiveness, respect and a feeling of self-worth. His behavior indicated a profound sense of responsibility for his own actions. He knew what he signified, and though he was always approachable, he held himself high.

He was not talkative. In meetings he seldom dominated the conversation, but respect for his knowledge and sound reason was so great that his suggestions were quickly accepted.

In everyday life he took good care of himself. To stay in shape he exercised and played golf often. Spectator sports held little interest for him. However, he liked the movies. "I like to go, sit in the dark and rest," he told one interviewer. In later years he put on weight, but retained an upright posture. As he aged his resemblance to his father became more and more apparent.

Music played an important part in his life. Despite deep involvement in his professional work he always found time to play the piano in the evenings, and he practiced for several hours on weekends. As a pianist he was a virtuoso. In addition to Chopin, his favorite composer, his repertoire included works by Bach ("I could play a few fugues from memory"), Mozart, Beethoven, Weber, Schumann and others. Among modern composers Rachmaninoff was a favorite. As a natural artist he sought expression and—in difficult times—solace in music. Such a combination of engineering and musical talent was, and still is, an exception in the American engineering world. In the interview he gave to the American musical monthly *The Etude*, he was quite outspoken in his views on training pianists and his own way of mastering the piano. There he mentioned also some of the piano virtuosos with whom he was acquainted: Marcelina Czartoryska, a princess who was a favorite pupil of Chopin and rarely gave public concerts; Maurycy Rosenthal; Antoni Rubinstein and Rubinstein's largely forgotten brother Nicholas among them. His primary interest was classical music.

Ignacy Morawski once related the story that during the 1930s he had gone to see Modjeski, when the engineer had suffered some business reverses. "It had something to do with one of the bridges, either in New Orleans or San Francisco. It was apparent that Modjeski was bothered by the outcome. That is when he sat down at the piano and began to play. He played Chopin. After an extended concert everyone felt better."[1] Music was his refuge. He would sit at the keyboard and polish away the day's cares. Then he would get up refreshed, ready to go on.

In Modjeski's life, in addition to music and work, there was always an important place for his family. His mother's death, however, had a significant impact on family relationships. It was she who kept alive the bonds between the American and Polish parts of the family, and the person who kept the family together in the United States.

Karol Chłapowski remained in Poland after his wife's funeral. Felix, Ralph's eldest son, became independent after his twentieth birthday. It happened under circumstances which should be mentioned because of the large expectations—probably unfulfilled—which the father had for his first-born. In February of 1907, two years before her death, Modjeska had written. "My grandson Felix is earn-

Family grouping: (from left) Felicie, Felix, Ralph Modjeski, Marylka, and Karolek (sitting).

ing his own bread, though he will be only twenty-one years old in August of the next year. The boy has energy and will be somebody."

But Felix decided to marry in 1908 despite his father's and his grandmother's disapproval. Karol Chłapowski, who rarely disagreed with his wife, held a differing opinion, writing to his brother that Felix "married not having reached the age of twenty-one. But I have hopes that this will come out well, as the young lady is very pleasant and kind (though her family is unsympathetic), while he works hard at his job."

Felix was married on June 2, 1908. His wife Jane Doty, gave birth to their son Felix on February 6, 1909. The new family was in less than enviable circumstances but moving on its own independent course. Relations were proper, but the hurried marriage may have moved father and son several degrees apart.

During this time Modjeski was alone. His younger son, Karolek,[2] was away at school, while his wife and daughter were travelling overseas. By 1912 he apparently reached the conclusion that reconciliation with his wife was not possible, they had moved too far apart. When Felicie returned to Chicago from the long visit abroad, they separated. It was a difficult time for all, but probably most difficult for the nineteen-year-old Marylka, who made some desperate attempts to bring her parents together but did not succeed. A reflection of these dark days may be found in her letters from this time.

During the next few years contact between family members was sporadic and full of tension. Even after 1916, when Ralph obtained a legal separation, family members still gathered at special events, and other attempts were made at reconciliation.

During this time a woman named Belle Silvera entered Modjeski's life. She was French by birth, a graphic artist teaching drawing at the Chicago Art Institute. Her favorite medium—pencil. Her favorite subject—bridges. One could also add, her favorite companion—Ralph Modjeski!

Her drawings must have made a deep impression on Ralph. Years later, in 1933, he sent her sketch of the Crooked River Bridge ("a wild place, the spot from which she drew had to be cleared of bushes and rattlesnakes") for publication in *Civil Engineering.*

In 1929 Belle Silvera committed suicide. The circumstances were never fully explained. The long lasting affair was surrounded with an atmosphere of scandal, which found its way into the newspapers and echoed through American society.[3]

One by one Ralph's children became independent. Felix Bozenta Modjeski, the eldest son, started his own business, Modjeski Electric Company, in Balboa, California. The business developed well and the financial position of his family improved significantly.

Karolek, the younger son, who by then called himself Charles, served in the United States Army in World War I, then obtained a degree in engineering from Cornell University. After his marriage to Ruth Phinney contact with his father became less frequent. First he settled in Harrisburg, Pennsylvania, but in 1927 he moved to Philadelphia. He worked as a civil engineer, for a time at Modjeski and Masters, but he was somewhat overshadowed by his father. His contribution to the firm was to serve as an engineer during the building of the Tacony-Palmyra Bridge. A frequent guest in his home on Penn Street was his mother Felicie, who maintained a close relationship with him.

At this time Ralph Modjeski was living in New York City in an apartment in Manhattan at 121 East 38th Street. In addition he had a fine apartment in Philadelphia at the Widener Building, and another on Jackson Street in Chicago. He moved around often, always maintaining at least two apartments.

His daughter, Marylka, remained closest to him. To her, Ralph Modjeski was very loving and always surrounded her with sincere, delicate care. Many of the warm letters that he wrote to her were preserved. The relationship continued after Marylka married (on June 15, 1920) Sidney Pattison, a Professor of English at the University of Arizona in Tucson. There Modjeski visited her, enjoying his grandchildren, Karolek (Karl) and Halka. Every visit at the Pattison home in Tucson, was an eagerly anticipated event as were his visits to their summer cottage in California, a few blocks from Felix's home.

Modjeski enjoyed watching his daughter work (she was an etcher, and later a painter) and she eagerly solicited his opinion. After spending a few days at her home he would return to New York recharged and relaxed. But Arizona was too far a distance to travel on a regular basis.

For some years Felicie refused to give her husband a formal divorce. First in Portland and then in Chicago, court proceedings continued, but the best that his lawyers could do was to obtain a legal separation.

The emotional temperature of the conflict remained high. Years passed but there was no resolution to the matter. Finally, in 1931 (at age seventy) he obtained a divorce in Reno, Nevada. On the next day he married Virginia Mary Giblyn, a person much younger than himself, reputedly a former cabaret performer. Virginia was a direct opposite of his first wife; she would not have made a good appearance at the Potocki Palace. However, she created a home for Ralph, one he needed at this time.

The matter received wide publicity, since the person at its core was a famous man. The American press, especially papers in New York City where Modjeski lived at the time, carried a complete description of the details, not without a trace of scandal. But the matter quickly passed, and future mention of Modjeski in the papers returned to praise for his engineering accomplishments.

Modjeski's late marriage no doubt threw a shadow over his relationships with his children and other family members. Yet in comparison to the previous destabilization of his life, Virginia Giblyn may have been treated as a lesser evil. In any case, his contacts with the family remained active.

Felix, Marylka, and Karolek as adults. Photograph courtesy of Halka Chronic.

Modjeski and his wife continued to live in New York. Even well into his seventies, he still often crossed the continent on professional and private matters. New York, San Francisco, and New Orleans are thousands of miles apart. But his mode of travel was different now—these were not the hurried dashes from work sites, but rather leisurely trips aboard more luxurious trains. Inspection visits to bridges in progress at New Orleans and San Francisco were separated by stays at resort towns such as Palm Springs. The tempo of his life had slowed down, as is normal for a person of his advanced years.

Virginia accompanied him on his journeys. Though the two of them visited Tucson together, stays at the Pattison home were not made in the same atmosphere of father-daughter visits of previous years.

Meanwhile, Felicie Modjeska continued to live as before, travelling with her companion Halina Dąbkowska. As before, she was happiest in Europe, and lived in Poland for a time. She also lived for some years in Tucson, with summers near Felix in

Felicie Benda Modjeski. Photograph courtesy of Halka Chronic.

California. Gradually succumbing to Parkinson's disease, she retained an active mind until her death in Philadelphia April 24, 1936.

In examining the lives of Ralph and his mother it would be difficult not to recount the things in their lives that have remained Polish, and those that became Americanized. Ralph Modjeski's entire life was bound to the American continent. After all it may be said that he made his choice of nationality at the time he changed his last name from Modrzejewski to Modjeski. This was understandable, but the choice of first name was exclusively his. It was something on the order of a "statement of principle." Much can also be inferred from the way he was listed in the registration book[4] for foreign students at the Ecole des Ponts et Chaussées. After his name is the note "Autrichen, naturalisé Americain." In the second part of the nineteenth century 71 of the 81 Poles who studied at the school gave their nationality as "Polonais."

Modjeski, however, never broke off contact with his native country, though visits there were less fre-

quent after his mother's death. When he spoke to his countrymen he always used proper Polish, and the letters he sent to Poland were signed with his full name—Rudolph Modrzejewski.

In contrast Kazimierz Gzowski, a Polish engineer who spent his life in Canada and made a career in bridge building there, was named to a committee to greet Ignacy Jan Paderewski in Toronto. When the two met, Gzowski wept, for he could not understand or reply to the great artist who addressed him in the Polish language.

This could never have happened to Modjeski.

Ignacy Morawski, writer and editor, who knew Modjeski in Chicago, wrote in a letter to Wiktor Kwast,

> Ralph Modjeski spoke proper Polish all his life. How could it be otherwise for a son of the great Polish tragedienne? But he had an accent that was strange and difficult to describe. It was not foreign, not one that you would find in a non-native speaker, but rather unusual. Some words he pronounced too clearly, like an actor. Aside from his speech, as to his Polishness, he was incontrovertibly a Pole, felt himself a Pole, and all those who knew him socially were aware of this.

His children, however, were brought up as Americans. He wanted them to live and work in the United States. When in 1905 Felix sought to study in Canada, Ralph the father was categorically opposed.

Marylka knew Polish well and kept up direct and heartfelt communications with family and friends in Poland. After World War II she made several trips to Kraków and Zakopane. Felix and Charles spoke Polish not as well but always conversed with their sister in that language. Their father wrote to them in English. Both grandmothers, Helena Modjeska as well as Felicie's mother Veronica Benda interjected some Polish spirit into their upbringing, but they remained essentially American. In this regard, the Modjeski family was little different from millions of other Polish immigrant families.

Modjeski's work was known in Poland, where his achievements generated enormous interest and respect in professional circles. He was occasionally mentioned in the press, and the Warsaw *Przegląd Techniczny* [Technical Review] in 1923 carried a cycle of articles about great American bridges, written by Professor Feliks Kucharzewski, also a graduate of the Ecole des Ponts et Chaussées. Kucharzewski often mentioned the impressive work of his Polish-American colleague.[5]

Many knew Modjeski's work indirectly, but a few learned about it in a direct way. Stefan Bryła, an enterprising instructor from the Lwów Polytechnic Institute, twenty-five years Modjeski's junior, came to America in 1912 and immediately visited the Quebec Bridge construction site. He learned the details of the bridge and then went on to see other great structures across the continent. Discussions with their designer must have been of great interest to him. Little wonder then, that he, like Modjeski himself, became infected with the romance of engineering.

Some years later, when Modjeski had built more and grander bridges and Stefan Bryła was a professor teaching in a reestablished and independent Poland, there came an opportunity to show his professional admiration for Modjeski's achievements. In the summer of 1929 after a twenty year absence, Modjeski again visited the land of his birth. In Poznań, at the Universal National Exhibition of Science and Industry [6] he received a medal from the Polish government. The award certificate stated, among other things, that he was being recognized for "a simplicity in [his] projects, which is the basis of true art."

In the following year, on June 4, a special gathering of the Lwów Polytechnic Institute Civil Engineering Department Council took place. Professor Stefan Bryła was invited by Dean Włodzimierz Stożek to explain his proposal for awarding an Honorary Doctoral Degree to Civil Engineer Ralph Modjeski-Modrzejewski for his contributions to the field of engineering, especially bridge building. On the same day, a general gathering of professors under the leadership of the Rector Kazimierz Bartel approved this proposal.

By this time Modjeski had left Poland. The official diploma was given to him in Washington, D.C. in February, 1931, by Tytus Filipowicz, Ambassador of the Polish Republic, a close associate of Józef Pilsudski, Marshal of Poland. The press noted that at the luncheon given by the ambassador to honor Modjeski on this occasion were representatives from the world of science and engineering, including the famous physicist James Brown Scott (secretary General of the Carnegie Foundation) and Mrs. Vernon Kellog. At that time an Honorary Doctoral Degree was also given to Paul Séjourné, a

Marylka Pattison.

French bridge builder, whom Modjeski had known during his studies at the Ecole des Ponts et Chaussées.

In his later years Modjeski became what is often called a "one man institution." His personal influence reached far outside the circle of persons connected with work or family.

His seventy-fifth birthday, January 27, 1936, was an outstanding social event as testified by the list of guests and the birthday greetings tendered. A decorative guest book from the occasion contains signatures of Othmar Ammann, Paul Cret, John E. Elliot, Daniel Moran, Leon S. Moisseiff, Montgomery B. Case, P. L. Pratley, and 169 other well known persons from engineering, science, business, and society.

Despite Ralph Modjeski's extraordinary vitality, in 1936 he handed over the helm of his engineering firm to Frank Masters and moved to California. After the completion of the San Francisco-Oakland Bay Bridge his professional involvement nearly ceased. As he neared the end of his life the energy visibly ebbed and he was quite happy to sit in a lawnchair and relax in the sun in the garden of his home at 157 N. Alexandria Ave. in Hollywood,

Bridge engineers Frank M. Masters, Jr. and his father Frank M. Masters in the shadow of the Benjamin Franklin Bridge on July 1, 1966. Photograph by Sam Kushner, courtesy of the Courier-Post.

where he spent his last years. He was temporarily revitalized by the company of his grandson Karl Pattison, son of his daughter Marylka, and visits by Marylka and her daughter Halka. He died in his home June 26, 1940, at seventy-nine years of age, and was buried at Inglewood Cemetery, Eternity Mausoleum.

His son Felix died a few months later preceding by four years the death of his younger son Charles and that of Sidney Pattison. The substantial estate left after Modjeski's death went to Virginia Giblyn. It was even impossible to recover family mementos. In 1966 Marylka Modjeska Pattison died as a result of an automobile accident on the eve of her departure for a summer in Poland. Her son Karl, a mechanical engineer, piloted a B-29 bomber during World War II and afterward worked for Hughes Aircraft in Tucson. He later joined the faculty of the University of Arizona. Her daughter Halka Chronic is a geologist.

Presently, as far as we know, there is only one living descendant of Ralph Modjeski in the male line. This is Thomas Modjeski, grandson of Felix. He lives in California.

Modjeski and Masters, Inc., the engineering company started by Ralph Modjeski, headquartered in Mechanicsburg, (near Harrisburg), Pennsylvania, continues to build bridges. After Ralph Modjeski stepped out of the firm it was administered by Frank Masters, who retired in 1972 at age ninety. He died two years later. The current chairman of the board is William B. Conway.

In recent years the firm designed a new bridge on the delta of the Mississippi near New Orleans. Again, the setting of the foundations was very difficult. The steel load-carrying structure has a large span for this type of construction, 376 meters or 1,234 feet. Modjeski's legacy still manifests itself in engineering and bridges which, like those built previously, give credit to the work of human hands and minds.

Chapter 8

At the Pinnacle of Fame

Modjeski was a true child of his uncertain, disordered but dynamic times— times that demanded special abilities and character traits, suited to the period and place in which he lived. Those were times of developing technology, when courage, hard work and knowledge led to success. He was industrious and had the necessary information at his disposal.

Modjeski's successes and accomplishments could hardly be called accidental. He was one of the people of that era who, despite wide interests, connected himself professionally with a relatively specialized field. He mustered his great intellectual resources for the development of bridge building taking full advantage of the great opportunities of his day. It is not surprising that he received recognition so many times during his lifetime. In his New York office an entire wall was hung with certificates, while a special glass cabinet contained medals and other awards.

But he kept these matters at a distance. Once he was asked about his awards. "Oh," he replied, "I have big ones and little ones. The big ones I received quite by accident, and the little ones were given to me because I already had the big ones!"

When Modjeski was fifty he received an Honorary Doctoral Degree from the University of Illinois at Urbana, in recognition for advancing the science of building steel bridges. Earlier, in 1927, he was awarded the same title from the Pennsylvania Military College (now Widener College) in Chester, Pennsylvania. Then yet another in Poland in 1930.

The Benjamin Franklin Institute in Philadelphia, which recognizes outstanding inventions and discoveries in the field of physics presented him with the Howard N. Potts Gold Medal in 1914, and eight years later awarded him the Franklin Medal, the highest award given in the United States for con-

tributions to the field of physics and their application. Together with the latter medal he received a certificate which made him an honorary member of the Institute. It was worded as follows:

> That the Franklin Medal be awarded to Ralph Modjeski, Civil Engineer, New York City, New York, in recognition of his signal achievements as a designer and builder of structures, mainly bridges, many of them epoch-making in the history of the engineering profession, beautiful as well as useful, involving on the part of the designer, vision, courage and technic of the highest order.

At the special gathering during which the medal was bestowed, Modjeski presented a lecture entitled: *Bridges Old and New, A Review of the History and Progress of Bridgebuilding.* At the same gathering the Franklin Medal was awarded to Joseph John Thompson, the English physicist and Nobel laureate who discovered the electron. In previous years recipients of the medal had included Heike Kamerlingh Onnes, for research in ultra-low temperatures, Thomas Alva Edison, and Charles A. Parsons, inventor of the steam turbine.

In September 1930, Modjeski received the John Fritz Gold Medal, "for significant accomplishments in the field of building large bridges, that were not only strong but beautiful." The committee awarding the medal was composed of leaders of the sixteen largest American engineering associations. Established in 1902, the award had previously been bestowed on Gugliemo Marconi, Lord Kelvin, and Herbert Hoover.

On February 25, 1931, at a gathering of leading industrialists, engineers, and scientists at the Palmer House Hotel in Chicago, Ralph Modjeski received the Washington Award, the highest recog-

The Benjamin Franklin Bridge.

nition that could be bestowed upon an engineer in the United States.[1] By statute the award was "recognition given to an engineer by his fellow engineers for special achievements whose purpose was to bring happiness and prosperity to mankind." It applies to all engineering disciplines and to scientific research, including science education. The ceremony was presided over by Elmer T. Howson, chairman of the special commission representing the largest American engineering associations (among them: Western Society of Engineers, American Institute of Mining and Metallurgical Engineers, American Society of Mechanical Engineers). The award was presented to Modjeski by W. O. Kurtz, president of the Western Society of Engineers. He spoke the following words on this occasion:

> The Washington Award in recognition of devoted, unselfish and preeminent service in advancing human progress. Conferred in 1931 upon Ralph Modjeski for his contribution to transportation through superior skill and courage in bridge design and construction.

Modjeski's acceptance speech reviewed the circumstances that led to his choosing the engineering profession.

Mr. President, Mr. Chairman, Ladies and Gentlemen: It is not fitting on this great occasion to speak very much about myself. I will only add to the brief outline that the Chairman has given of my life by saying how I became an engineer and why.

When I was four years old I got hold of a screwdriver. This gave me an idea. I immediately investigated what this screwdriver was for and practiced on a door lock of the drawing room of the house we lived in and took it all apart. I could not put it together again. And my father said "You will be an engineer."

I persisted in that until, as the Chairman said, I failed in the examination for entrance to the Ecole des Ponts et Chaussées where there were 25 places and 100 candidates. Then for about six months I practiced music six and eight hours a day. After six months I began to think, and at the end of six months had thought out my problem and joined the preparatory school and three months later I passed the examination into the Ecole des Ponts et Chaussées.

This is a great honor. I do not know how to express my gratitude to all the gentlemen who have awarded it to me. I prize it very highly; I prize it higher than any award I have received heretofore. And, ladies and gentlemen, I thank you.

The George Washington Bridge on the Hudson River, built by Othman Ammann. Postcard from the 1930s.

To properly convey the atmosphere at this gathering it should be mentioned that later in the program Ralph Budd, president of the Great Northern Railway Corporation, the largest rail organization of the midwest, also gave an eloquent address.

In receiving the Washington Award, Modjeski found himself in good company. Before him, in 1927, the award had been presented to Orville Wright for his achievements in aviation; after him in 1936 it went to Charles F. Kettering, automotive inventor (electric starter, lighting) and president of General Motors Corporation.

Modjeski received the Washington Award not only as an outstanding engineer. His achievements had pioneered unknown areas of his field, and had already been recognized by a different sphere of professional people: for contributions in developing the engineering sciences he was made a member of the National Academy of Sciences in 1929.

Though he built only on the American continent, he was also famous in Europe. He took part in the World Exposition in Paris in 1900 where he received a gold medal. In 1926 the government of France elected him to membership in their distinguished Legion of Honor.

His international reputation was such that the government of the Soviet Socialist Republics asked him to submit a design for a building to house the

Supreme Soviet in Moscow. It was to be a massive building 400 meters (1,312 feet) high with a huge statue of Lenin on top. Modjeski did not turn down this challenge, and a preliminary design was drawn up in his office in 1935. The full project, however, was not completed.

That same year the government of Turkey asked him to conduct a study on the possibility of bridging the Bosporus at Istanbul. His analysis showed that this was feasible and initiated a series of undertakings that, in the 1970s, led to the largest suspension bridge in Europe at the time.

During his busy, useful life Modjeski expressed himself mainly through his work, as a sculptor does through objects he creates. Nevertheless he found time to write about thirty significant technical publications. In 1897 he produced two large monographs on special problems connected with the building of the bridge over the Mississippi at Rock Island. His last paper, published in 1929, was entitled *Suspension Bridges with Special Reference to the Philadelphia-Camden Bridge.* It was presented as a lecture at the World Engineering Congress in Japan in 1930 where Modjeski was the chief representative of engineers from the United States.

His other published works covered a wide variety of subjects relating to analysis of problems in design and construction of large bridges, and to the

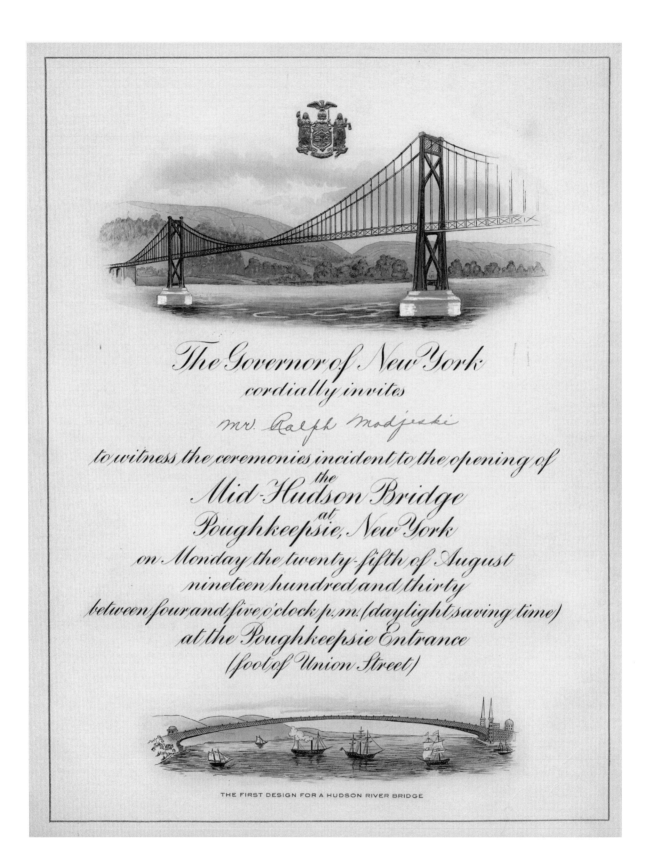

The Governor of New York
cordially invites

Mr. Ralph Modjeski

to witness the ceremonies incident to the opening of
the
Mid-Hudson Bridge
at
Poughkeepsie, New York
on Monday the twenty-fifth of August
nineteen hundred and thirty
between four and five o'clock p.m. (daylight saving time)
at the Poughkeepsie Entrance
(foot of Union Street)

THE FIRST DESIGN FOR A HUDSON RIVER BRIDGE

Invitation to the Mid-Hudson Bridge Opening. Courtesy of Frank M. Masters, Jr.

use of steel and reinforced concrete in engineering (he was one of the few builders who designed bridges from both materials). Among his papers is *High Level Fixed Bridges over Navigable Waters*, published by the American Association of Port Authorities addressing important parameters that must be considered in designing bridges under which ships must pass. That same year, 1927, he published "Unusual Problems in Design and Construction of Large Bridges" in the *Journal of the Franklin Institute*. It discusses various problems, based on his experience in the field, which must be solved by the engineer at every phase of his work, from selecting the site, through bridge design, to completing construction.

Modjeski's most important published work is probably the 1913 report, *Design of Large Bridges with Special Reference to the Quebec Bridge*, where based on lessons learned from the catastrophe he gives his insights into the construction of large cantilever bridges. Worthy of note is *Special Problems in Bridge Design and Construction* published in the Aldred Lecture Series, at the Massachusetts Institute of Technology.

Fifty years in engineering is a long career. From such a career one can readily estimate an engineer's lifetime contribution to the development of technology. Such assessment places Modjeski among those who have led the field of construction technology in the last century. He was responsible for many advances in bridge building around the world, advances that have brought about changes and developments in other fields of civil engineering.

Modjeski's accomplishments in design and construction are of the first order. His career confirms the maxim that development in the field of bridge construction is accelerated through the building of structures, not through theory. Today, development in this field starts with a designer's work based on the current state of the art, with the added involvement of personal judgement, knowledge, and boldness. Detailed theoretical analysis precedes the completion of precedent breaking structures, but at some point the engineer must leave the comfort of the tried and true and extrapolate theory in order to extend the borders of the possible.

In pre-technology days, however, bridges were built by courageous, hardy men who had an instinctive grasp of technical matters, dealing with the unknown by using rules handed down by tra-

A note written by Ralph Modjeski in Polish to Alfred Nieżychowski. "December 14, 1929. Dear Alfred. On returning from Japan I found your letter. I am sorry that because of my trip to the Far East I could not be in Detroit to attend the opening of the bridge. I do not know when an opportunity to be there will arise. I would very much like to meet your wife. I believe that this will soon be possible. Best regards to the both of you. Happy Holidays and a good New Year. With true friendship, Ralph Modjeski."

dition, without benefit of a technical education as we know it today. They conquered difficulties through hard work, arriving at their goals by using common sense trial and error techniques.

The builder of the first large steel bridge in America (the first to span the Mississippi), was self-taught James Eads. Kazimierz Gzowski, a Polish-born engineer who made a name for himself building bridges in Canada, was a Pennsylvania lawyer.

Ralph Modjeski in a portrait made in 1932. This photograph was dedicated to Frank M. Masters. Courtesy of Frank M. Masters, Jr.

Modjeski's first employer, George Morison held a diploma from Harvard University, in law.[2] One of Europe's finest bridge engineers, Thomas Telford, was a journeyman bricklayer in his youth, whereas Francois Hennebique was a mason by trade.

The builder of the famous suspension bridge over the Menai Strait in Wales, Robert Stephenson, started his career in mining and railroading and built bridges only near the end of his life.

A new era began in bridge building with the introduction of steel as a main structural material, toward the end of the nineteenth century. Initially, this expensive material was used only in small quantities to design structures in which the distribution of forces was clear and could be predicted with certainty. Steel helped these structures to develop; and the development of statics as a science permitted precise calculation of the forces involved. (Rankine published his *Applied Mechanics* in 1858 and Cullman followed with *Graphische Statik* seven years later.) Engineering had to wait for theoreticians like Cullman, Dupuit and Winkler to

formulate principles which the builders could use to design their structures. Among those who benefited from this work were two Poles who worked outside their home country—Stanisław Kierbedź, working in Russia,[3] and (fifty years later) Ralph Modjeski in America.

If one were to sum up the contributions Ralph Modjeski made to bridge building in a few sentences, three areas should be mentioned.

• Modjeski increased the spans of truss and suspension bridges. The main span of the bridge at Metropolis was the longest truss until 1974; the Quebec Bridge still holds the world's record in its class. Several Modjeski bridges remain among the largest, even though over seventy years have passed since their construction. His suspension bridges at Philadelphia and Detroit were the longest on their completion. The San Francisco-Oakland Bay Bridge set no records for the length of its spans (either suspension or cantilever), but its total length and rapidity of construction added up to a magnificent feat that inspired the world's admiration. It demonstrated engineering capabilities and organizational talents of the highest caliber.

• Modjeski introduced new steel alloys into bridge construction—alloys with improved strength and durability. After early experiments with steel alloys conducted by Eads and Lindenthal, it was Modjeski who used alloy steels in large quantities and in rational ways. In addition to nickel steel he was the first bridge engineer to use silicon steel with its good strength characteristics, advantageous price, and other beneficial qualities. It should be stressed that he used alloy steels in large constructions, mostly record setters, but not in small, less significant structures. Among large bridges that benefitted most were those at Metropolis, Quebec, and Philadelphia.

• Modjeski applied simplifications to structural construction design both in secondary stiffening members and main load-carrying beams in truss bridges; he introduced improvements to suspension bridge technology, notably steel pylons that were used in a rational thought-out, integrated form and advancements in the design of cable configurations and deck-stiffening beams. His early bridges show a logical, then-innovative regular layout of cross braces. The articulated continuous bridge was first introduced in America by Morison, to minimize the effect of settling foundations. It

January 20, 1936.

Mr. Ralph Modjeski,
52 Vanderbilt Avenue,
New York City.

Dear Mr. Modjeski :

     Our acquaintance and collaboration of fifteen years
have been one of the landmarks of my career.

     Renan once said that what creates a nation is the memory
of past accomplishments and the will to add to these in the future.
This is what binds individuals more strongly than material interests.

     I feel this particularly today when the occasion of your
approaching anniversary recalls to me the work I had the pleasure to
do under your guidance, and I hope that an already long list is by
no means complete. You have given to all your collaborators the
example of the highest professional conscience and of constant striv-
ing for greater perfection.

     My associates wish to add their compliments to mine, and
unite in wishing you many years of this admirable activity which has
placed you at the front of your profession.

               Very sincerely yours,

               Paul P. Cret

PPC/W

Letter from Paul P. Cret sent to Ralph Modjeski on his seventieth birthday. From the collection of Ralph Modjeski Pattison.

was his young assistant, however, who brought this form of construction to a level that has not been exceeded since. Today, the pylons on the bridges in Philadelphia and Detroit are accepted as conventional, but at the time of their completion they were considered innovative and ahead of their time. To understand this one only has to look at the cable-supporting towers of the George Washington Bridge.[4] The significance of deck-stiffening beams was recognized by Ralph Modjeski years before the bridge disaster at Tacoma Narrows. The design he chose to use on his bridges—a Warren Truss with regularly spaced cross bracing—is now standard on most suspension bridges.

Modjeski also made a contribution in expanding the spans of drawbridges and in introducing new designs. The double bascule drawbridge in the Tacony-Palmyra Bridge is still one of the largest of its type, and from its engineering aspects, one of the most interesting.

There are few engineers in history whose contribution to theory, and especially construction, was so great and had so many facets. Working mainly in the field of large steel bridge construction Modjeski also influenced the development of concrete bridge construction in the United States, as exemplified by the concrete approach spans in the bridge at Thebes. He contributed to progress in the methodology of building deep underwater foundations as shown by the deeply set piers for the bridges in San Francisco and New Orleans.

Even as he contributed to the quality of bridge building, Modjeski produced an amazing quantity of bridges. At the time of his death newspapers have calculated the total length of all the bridges he built to be 125 miles or 200 kilometers, at an aggregate cost close to 200 million dollars, an enormous sum in 1940. In today's dollars it would be over ten times as much. It is doubtful that there was anyone before or after him who could boast such numbers!

Viewing Modjeski's life from an engineering point of view is too narrow a way of appraising the man and his accomplishments. To build a bridge involves more than doing an analysis of the problem, performing the necessary calculations, developing a set of drawings, and supervising a construction project.

In addition there is a field mastered by only a few: gauging social conditions and economic possibilities, and making the appropriate decisions often at the risk of position and fortune. During his career Modjeski signed contracts valued at many millions of dollars, engaged contractors, and assured that safety conditions and deadlines were met. This last aspect played an enormous role. The marketplace tolerated only those who delivered. Modjeski was not only an engineer. He was also a businessman, an organizer, and whether he wanted to be or not, a social activist.

This is where this story ends. But the few chapters written about Modjeski's technical and scientific achievements cannot convey that which underlay his success. They can say little about the ongoing effort, the ideas and experiments, that were combined with knowledge learned at the world's best civil engineering school. They cannot say anything about that which was most important under these conditions, about the endurance and courage which Modjeski had to muster in order to complete his ambitious and innovative structures.

Notes

Preface

1. Leopold Infeld, *Quest*, Chelsea Publishing Company, New York, 1980.

2. *Funk and Wagnall's New Encyclopedia*, New York, 1983.

3. Bridges built by Nebuchadnezzar II and his successor Nabonid as well as about other leaders involved in bridge building are described in J. Głomb's book *Pontifex Maximus*, published in Polish, Gliwice, 1997.

4. Judith Dupre, *Bridges*, Black Dog and Leventhal Publishers, New York, 1997.

5. *Ibid.*

6. Bill M, *Robert Maillard*, Girsberger, Zurich, 1965.

7. Warsaw University of Technology had two Chairs of Bridge Building: one led by F. Szelągowski, another by Z. Wasiutyński. The Wasiutyński chair had II (Roman Numeral Two) in front of the name.

8. Those students were admitted in 1952. At that time Warsaw University of Technology (Politechnika Warszawska), offered two general degrees in engineering: BS after four years and MS after five and one-half years of study.

9. Usually civil engineers work in the shadow of architects. The commonly known designers of skyscrapers, churches, museum buildings, railroad stations, concert halls, etc., are architects. Structural engineers are superseded by the architect's fame. Quite often, however, especially in cases of tall buildings and other complicated structures, it is an injustice for civil engineers whose creative contribution is at least as important as the contribution of architects. The exceptions are designers of highways, railroad tracks, tunnels, and canals and, of course, bridges, where civil engineers are listed as main designers of the project. In the case of bridge design, the architects are coworkers of structural engineers. They contribute toward the general look of the structure, appearance of pylons, kinds of support stone, color of paints, ornaments and decorations, bridge entrance portals as well as surroundings of the bridge. When Ralph Modjeski designed bridges in Pennsylvania, he did so in cooperation with the illustrious Philadelphia architect Paul Phillippe Cret. P. P. Cret was an admirer of Modjeski's bridge design knowledge and skills. In one of his letters he expressed his admiration for Modjeski and thanked him for giving him the opportunity to "work under his guidance."

10. In 1898, Maria (Marie) Skłodowska Curie (1867–1934), a Polish physicist, who with her husband Pierre Curie, performed fundamental works on radiation and discovered two new elements: radium and polonium.

11. Leopold Infeld, *op. cit., See note 1.*

12. Habilitation in some European universities is a degree above Ph.D. Traditionally it is granting the doctor the right to lecture at the university that has given the title.

13. Józef Głomb, *About Determinants of the Contemporary Times*, (O Wyznacznikach Współczesności), in Polish, published by the Center for Science Popularization of the Polish Academy of Science, Warsaw, 1999.

Chapter 1

1. Poles living under the Austrian administration were not allowed to build a monument to their national hero, who had led an insurrection in 1794 to free them from foreign domination. They fell back on the ancient custom of contributing soil to a mound in honor of a chieftain.

2. His actual name was Sinnmayer, but he used the Polish form of the name: Zimajer.

3. Probably invented by Zimajer, who over the next few years would also use the name. "Modrzew" is Polish for larch or tamarack tree.

4. The matter is recorded in Chlędowski's journals. He was then a student at the Kraków academy. His opinion of Zimajer was negative, not surprising as the young student was a fevered fan of the beautiful Helena. The information about the content of the agreement is no doubt accurate. The man who would later become a Minister of the Austro-Hungarian Empire was then an intern at Machalski's law office and one of the witnesses to the signing.

5. The January 22, 1863, insurrection was one of several attempts to wrest control by force of arms of the eastern portion of Poland, then under Russian control. It failed, and many of its participants were imprisoned or exiled to Siberia. Poland would not become independent again until 1918 following the efforts of Ignacy Jan Paderewski, Józef Pilsudski and other Polish patriots.

6. Henryk Sienkiewicz (1846–1916), one of Poland's great writers, helped to create the historical novel genre. His adventure stories, set in Poland's golden past, inspired many generations of Poles. He won the Nobel Prize for *Quo Vadis?* a novel of Nero's imperial Rome. This book was made into a Hollywood film in 1953 and re-filmed in Poland in 2000.

7. The Centennial Exposition in Philadelphia celebrated the 100th anniversary of the signing of the Declaration of Independence.

8. Charles Fourier published his utopian concept of freely existing cooperatives of craftsmen in 1800.

Chapter 2

1. Five years later Bolesław Prus, another famous Polish writer, would join the chorus praising Modjeska's talents.

2. Georges Eugene Hausmann was chief of city planning from 1853 to 1870. Thanks to the support of Napoleon III, he managed to realize a great many of his plans for the city in the 1860s.

3. This information is not absolutely certain. Some sources state that Ralph Modjeski was naturalized on September 7, 1887, while his mother took citizenship two years later.

4. Helena Zimajer-Rapacka gave this interview to a Warsaw evening paper, the *Kurier Czerwony* [Red Courier] in 1936. After World War II she gave another interview in London.

5. Ralph and Felicie were less closely related than most cousins. Ralph's mother and Felicie's father were half-brother and half-sister, with only one parent in common. Nevertheless, social and religious protocol required that they obtain a Papal dispensation which was done before their marriage.

6. Ralph was already twenty-four years old.

7. Felicie was born on February 2, 1868. She was not yet 18.

8. Delmonico's continues as a New York institution. It moved uptown, together with the fashionable part of New York City, and is still counted among the city's best restaurants.

Chapter 3

1. This title might have been somewhat overstated. Though Morison's qualifications and achievements are undeniable, there is no doubt room in the bridge builders' pantheon for several other outstanding early engineers including Squire Whipple, the Roeblings (father and son), and James Eads.

2. The city of Wieliczka in southern Poland is famous for salt mining. The mines have operated since the eighteenth century. They are a major tourist attraction and many worked-out chambers have been artistically carved into chapels and ballrooms lit by rock-salt chandeliers.

3. At street level the walls are nearly two meters thick.

4. This data is from a Western Society of Engineers (WSE) paper that provides description of a trip to Thebes and Carbondale, Illinois, October 29–31, 1903. In 1903 Modjeski was President of WSE and invited members with their families to inspect the Thebes Bridge. This article provides a detailed description of the Thebes Bridge.

Chapter 4

1. These were the words used by a reporter writing for the *St. Louis Post Dispatch* on January 10, 1926.

2. The Roman engineer Vitruvius wrote about the precursors of caissons made of oak, but it was

Eads who made the first large scale modern application of this technology on his bridge over the Mississippi.

3. There was some justification for the initial doubt. The Manhattan Bridge was designed by Leon S. Moisseiff using his own method for calculating deflection in suspension bridges. It was the beginning of this outstanding engineer's career. Moisseiff's last project, however, a suspension bridge over Tacoma Narrows known as "Galloping Gertie" was destroyed in 1940, only a few months after completion, due to excessive deflection during a storm.

4. Speaking of the work tempo—an article by Modjeski describing the events appeared a month later in the February 1912 issue of the Chicago biweekly *Engineering News*.

5. The record lasted until 1931, when Othmar Ammann completed the Bayonne Bridge over the Kill van Kull narrows between Staten Island and New Jersey.

6. One of Cooper's books, *General Specifications for Steel Highway and Electric Railway Bridges and Viaducts*, was published in five editions and was the main handbook on the subject at the time, and not only in America. Already in 1879, he had prepared the first set of standards and published them for the Erie Railway Co.

7. At the time this was the world's longest bridge and was the pride of British engineering. It fell eighteen months after construction ended (in 1878).

8. The Quebec Bridge is listed in the *Guinness Book of World Records* (1998) as the Longest Cantilever Bridge—1,800 feet between piers, 3,239 feet overall.

Chapter 5

1. This friendship stood the test of time. Ignacy Morawski stated that even in the 1930s he would see Marcella Sembrich—then the baroness Stein—at Ralph's New York apartment. He also witnessed her great success on the stage at Carnegie Hall.

Chapter 6

1. This document, an outstanding example of the calligrapher's art, is bound in leather. It is in the possession of Modjeski's great-grandson, Ralph Modjeski Pattison of Tucson, Arizona.

2. Since 1911 he held the title of Doctor Honoris Causa from the University of Illinois at Urbana.

3. In 1989 the concrete deck was replaced with steel plate decking. The work was completed without closing the bridge down to traffic.

4. These heat treated cable wires, used before only on one bridge, were found to have a brittleness that caused some to crack during installation. Consequently they were replaced by the standard type wire used in suspension cables.

5. The interurban railway tracks on the lower deck were converted to automobile lanes in 1948. Currently the upper deck and the lower deck carry five lanes of traffic each.

6. During a severe earthquake on October 17, 1989, a section of the upper deck collapsed onto the lower level. While it was rapidly repaired and continues to serve, plans were drawn up to replace the cantilever bridge with a suspension span.

7. The tunnel through Yerba Buena Island is listed in the *Guinness Book of World Records* (1998) as the Largest Road Tunnel because of its dimensions—width: 77 ft. 10 in., height: 56 ft., length 540 ft.

8. The San Francisco-Oakland Bay Bridge is listed in the *Guinness Book of World Records* (1998) as the busiest bridge—used by an average 274,000 vehicles a day in 1996, a total of 100 million vehicles per year.

9. The AISC is dedicated to the development of steel construction in the United States, and gives recognition to the best engineering solutions that use steel, taking into consideration the esthetic values.

10. The bridge was listed in the *Guinness Book of World Records* in 1981 as the world's longest combination rail and automobile bridge. This record has since been surpassed.

Chapter 7

1. It should be added that this story was related sixty years after the event. Morawski added "In my consideration he rates highly. Though he was an engineer, sometimes he behaved like a poet."

2. Karolek is diminutive for Karol, which is Polish for Charles.

3. It was reported in the newspapers that a suicide note was found. It contained a statement from Belle Silvera that she was suffering from a debilitating disease which might leave her in a state of

paralysis and that she took her life as not to be a burden to anyone.

4. Registre matricule No. 1 des Eleves Externes de l'ENPC–1882

5. Kucharzewski graduated from the Ecole des Ponts et Chaussées in 1872, thirteen years before Modjeski.

6. This exhibition later became the International Poznań Trade Fair which still takes place every year.

Chapter 8

1. The entire ceremony is described in the *Journal of the Western Society of Engineers*, April 1, 1931, p. 69. In the article it is noted that the presentation of the award to Ralph Modjeski was followed by "prolonged applause."

2. In America, lawyers proved remarkably able in transitioning to engineering careers. Another lawyer, Thaddeus Hyat, was the first in America to conduct studies on the strength of reinforced concrete beams and slabs. He published the results in 1877 as *An Account of Some Experiments with Portland Cement Concrete Combined with Iron as a Building Material.*

3. Stanisław Kierbedź, a Polish born engineer (1810–1899) built a number of bridges in Russia, including the first bridge over the Neva River in St. Petersburg.

4. The towers of the George Washington Bridge were to be faced with stone, to evoke the spirit—if not the appearance—of earlier suspension bridges. The economic depression of 1929 and consequent lack of funds for this purely decorative detail caused them to remain uncovered.

Offices of Modjeski and Masters, Inc. in Mechanicsburg, Pennsylvania. Photograph courtesy of Modjeski and Masters, Inc.

Acknowledgments

Afterword - Edition I

This book in which I tried to present the life and work of Ralph Modjeski, could not have been written without the kindness and help of many people. First, I would like to thank Jerzy Got and Józef Szczublewski, who have freely shared much information and allowed me to use interesting materials concerning the life of Ralph Modjeski. I was also able to use their published works about Helena Modrzejewska.

I also owe thanks to Janusz Benedyktowicz, Stefan Bratkowski, Andrzej Chiczewski, Dezydery Chłapowski, Karol Malcharek, Stanisław Kosch, Kazimierz Wysiatycki and Karol Zuda who also provided me with valuable materials and information.

Wiktor Kwast has worked untiringly for many years to bring the person of Ralph Modjeski to life for readers on both sides of the Atlantic. Thanks to his in-depth research many details from the life and work of this brilliant engineer are known. I was able to learn much from the information he had gathered. I thank him for the kindness in allowing me to use these materials.

During the writing of the book I consulted many different published works. In addition to the memoir of Helena Modjeska *(Memories and Impressions)*, and the works of Got and Szczublewski, I consulted the novel by Tymon Terlecki *Pani Helena* [Lady Helena], the books by Marion Moore Coleman *(Fair Rosalind)*, the memoirs of W. F. Durand, and journals of Kazimierz Chlędowski, Ignacy Paderewski and others. I also was able to use the research of Bolesław Orłowski and his valuable remarks and suggestions, which he shared with me after reading the draft manuscript. For reading the initial draft and words of encouragement I thank

Professor Stefan Kaufman.

I obtained much valuable information about Ralph Modjeski's work from the Modjeski and Masters, Inc. in Harrisburg, thanks to Russel Stearns, while data about Modjeski's student days at the Ecole des Ponts et Chaussées I obtained from Henryk Wojciechowski.

In preparing this text for printing I had a great deal of help from Teresa Matuszkiewicz and Lucja Promny.

Gliwice, March 1980

Afterword - Edition II

After the first edition of this book appeared I visited the United States several times. There, I had the opportunity to obtain various research materials. Among those with whom I spoke were people who knew Modjeski personally. Especially informative were my conversations with Ignacy Morawski in New York. Despite his advanced age he gave me several hours of his time and spoke about the "old days." I would like to thank him for his stories, and the interesting information he presented, but especially for the opportunity to make contact with history in a direct way. I would also like to thank Wiktor Kwast of Tucson, Arizona, who shared his knowledge and some of the materials at his disposal.

After the first edition appeared in Poland, and was serialized twice in Polish-language newspapers in America, I received many letters from readers. These contained valuable opinions and some new information. The reviews which appeared on both sides of the Atlantic were also most valuable.

This caused me to rework the book. This edition is significantly different from the initial one. It is slightly longer. I changed nearly half the text and many of the illustrations. The character of the book has not changed, but there is additional information and a stronger link to the historical background.

The opportunity for making these changes I owe to Polonia Publishing, which approached me about the possibility of creating a new edition, and to the Kosciuszko Foundation in New York, especially Wiesław Juszczak and Maryla Janiak, thanks to whom I was able to obtain much new and interesting material.

Rycerka Górna, July 1986

Bridges on Stamps

Ralph Modjeski's work has appeared on stamps several times, for example the Quebec Bridge and the San Francisco-Oakland Bay Bridge (above). In 1999 the Republic of Poland honored him with a commemorative stamp that shows the Benjamin Franklin Bridge and his portrait at approximately fifty yeas of age.

Translator's Note

Every project has a moment of conception—this book was no different, except in this case I remember exactly when it happened. The critical moment was when, after returning from a trip to California, my "part-time employer" Edward Pinkowski, a respected Polish-American historian, handed me a small volume and asked, "Do you think you could translate this?"

After reading the book, the first edition of Prof. Józef Głomb's biography of Ralph Modjeski, I decided that it would be a most worthwhile project. One motivating factor was the fact that despite his tremendous accomplishments in bridge design, Ralph Modjeski's name had been nearly forgotten, and the seventy-fifth anniversary of the Benjamin Franklin Bridge was quickly approaching! Another was the fact that there was so much misinformation about Ralph Modjeski in circulation in the Polish-American press and literature. One guidebook printed in Poland named him as the designer of the Golden Gate Bridge (it was really built by Joseph B. Strauss). A newspaper article had him building the Panama Canal with General George W. Goethals; another ascribed the Pulaski Skyway to his engineering genius. I could not find anything to support these last two contentions, and certainly Prof. Głomb found nothing like that while doing his research.

Shortly thereafter, during a trip to Poland, I met the author, Prof. Józef Głomb and he provided me with a copy of the second edition of his book and a letter allowing me to do the translation. Little did I know then, that the affable gentleman with whom I was speaking was one of, if not the top, authority on bridge building in Poland. The short listing in *Poland: An Encyclopedic Guide* gives one a good idea of his many qualifications: "Civil Engineer; Profes-sor at the Silesian Technical University; Member of the Polish Academy of Sciences (PAN); designer of large constructions, mainly bridges; research in the field of civil engineering, bridge building, as well as the history and philosophy of engineering."

After translating two chapters and sending them to various publishers I found that there was no interest in the book. Neither commercial publishers, university publishers, nor even so-called "Polonia" publishers wanted to take this book into print. That is when our Philadelphia Chapter of the Kosciuszko Foundation decided to become involved, and finance publication by selling ads in the back of the book.

Soon we were being contacted by our friends from all over the United States asking about the book and supporting it actively. But there were difficulties as well. Prof. Głomb was not able to recover the original illustrations from his Warsaw publisher after the second Polish edition was printed in 1988. Fortunately, Mrs. Halka Chronic, Ralph Modjeski's granddaughter, whom Prof. Głomb recruited to act as the editor for the American edition, was willing to share her family album photos. Other contributions of photographs followed, including a portrait of Ralph Modjeski and bridge photos from the Modjeski and Masters firm (my thanks to William P. Conway and Michael Britt). Another portrait and other items came from the collection of Frank Masters, Jr., a retired engineer and son of Frank Masters, Ralph Modjeski's partner.

Edward Pinkowski's voluminous files on figures from Polish-American history gave me more insight into Ralph Modjeski and his work. Thanks to Mr. Pinkowski I had access to other individuals who had materials on hand. From Thomas Duszak, in addition to some interesting photos, I received a rare reminiscence about Ralph Modjeski written by Harry Engel (1905–1988), a onetime employee of the Modjeski and Masters firm.

RALPH MODJESKI - A Reminiscence

I first met Ralph Modjeski in early 1927 when, having finished participating in a preliminary field survey for the proposed Tacony-Palmyra Bridge over the Delaware, and having thereafter inspected the test borings along the proposed alignment, I was brought into the Philadelphia office of Modjeski, Masters and Chase to work on the preliminary design under the resident partner, Clement Chase. The Philadelphia office would then be visited at intervals by Mr. Masters from his own Harrisburg office in the Keystone Building, and by Mr. Modjeski on trips from his New York office. On one such visit by Mr. Modjeski at which he saw the preliminary sketches that had been made, Mr. Chase graciously invited me to go to lunch with himself and Mr. Modjeski. I was, needless to say, in proper awe of the noted engineer who, with the slight paunch connoting dignity in those days before the physical fitness movement, impressed me with his brevity of speech, always to the point.

The preliminary plan for Tacony-Palmyra having received sufficient approval by September of 1927, I was transferred then to Mr. Modjeski's New York office at 121 East 38th Street to work on the final design. This New York office was in Mr. Modjeski's private home, a brownstone row house, with stone steps up to the first floor where all the work was done, and a basement entrance several steps down below sidewalk level where the employees entered. Mr. Modjeski lived in the upper floors.

The first floor, our working floor, had a conference room in front, then an executive office for Glenn Woodruff, the Principal Assistant Engineer, and his secretary-bookkeeper, Miss Tracy, plus another secretary, and finally at the rear in a remodeled kitchen, our drafting room. This former kitchen had room for about ten drafting tables crowded together, with a window in the rear wall supplying north light, augmented by a gooseneck incandescent lamp on each table.

Mr. Modjeski would come down from his living quarters to discuss design with Glenn Woodruff and make occasional "tours" of the drafting tables with him, and to have special meetings, sometimes with clients, in the front conference room. He conveyed, in all this, an air of distinction which was clearly his due. He had

been Chief Engineer and Chairman of the Board of Engineers for the design and construction of the Delaware River Bridge at Philadelphia (now the Ben Franklin Bridge) which, at its opening in 1926, had set a new main span record of 1750 feet; and he was now Chairman of the Board of Engineers for the proposed San Francisco-Oakland Bay Bridge. Preliminary design studies for the latter bridge were at that time under way in the New York office, mostly by George Randall under the supervision of Glenn Woodruff. It was George's own idea to use a common anchorage to tie together the two equal suspension bridges that were eventually built; I can remember George's explanation to me, the neophyte in the office, that the opposing pulls from the twin bridges would balance each other so that the required deep anchorage at that location would not need to be as massive as might be supposed.

George's table was right behind me, receiving the best light from the window of the former kitchen, and behind him sat Y. L. Wang, later to join us in the Harrisburg office. Also, at tables alongside mine were Barney Dietrich who stayed with us until the 1940s, and Tien Kuo who became an Associate. Among the other five draftsmen was Howard Topping, who is mentioned only because he left later to work on the San Francisco-Oakland Bay Bridge under Glenn Woodruff when the latter became Engineer of Design in California as Mr. Modjeski's personal appointee. Woodruff's departure left George Randall to take over in the New York office as Principal Assistant Engineer of the firm.

I was in the New York office from September of 1927 to July, 1928 when, the contract plans of Tacony-Palmyra having been finished, contracts let, and checking of contractor's details under way, I was dispatched to Ambridge, Pennsylvania, to be an inspector of the Tacony-Palmyra steel fabrication in the American Bridge Company plant there.

But that time in the New York office remains memorable to me because of all that was going on. Besides the work already cited, there was the checking of contractor's details for the Mid-Hudson suspension bridge at Poughkeepsie on which, unfortunately, one of the foundation caissons had tipped over (and Woodruff was to devise the means for righting it) while the contract plans for the Louisville Bridge over the Ohio River were also being prepared.

In all this, Glenn Woodruff was our inspiring force, into everything. Our crew of ten men under his guidance made our calculations in neat tables on 8.5 by 11 coordinate paper, using slide rules, and adding "by hand" (checking the additions ourselves by afterward adding *down* the column), all without the benefit of even the then common-enough mechanical calculating machine (we had none). It was, I think, Mr. Modjeski's own philosophy, as conveyed to us in Glenn Woodruff's training, that a bridge design had to be thought through *personally*.

In the drafting room, we would sometimes hear Mr. Modjeski playing the piano upstairs, excellently of course; but this would usually be heard only if we lagged around after closing hours. And this leads naturally into my final recollection of Mr. Modjeski in this period.

I had been working late, on my own, trying to finish a calculation, when he came downstairs, saw the light at my drafting table, came over and said quite kindly "Don't you think you'd better go home now?"

And I did.

Other materials and articles came into my possession as I continued to work on producing a good English language text. One newspaper report sheds an interesting light on the humanitarian aspects of Ralph Modjeski's personality. This article, entitled "Ralph Modjeski Is Man Who Really Built Bridge" from *The Philadelphia Record*, July 4, 1926, explains many of the cost-saving features of the Benjamin Franklin Bridge, but the final paragraph dwells on the life saving features of the construction.

> Another important invention which figured in the early days of bridge construction was the one of safety chambers capable of holding 100 men in the caissons while they were being sunk. Had a sudden rush of water poured into the caisson through some accident the safety chambers would have acted as diving bells.

This strongly suggests that Ralph Modjeski valued human life more than money, when he designed these essential elements of the bridge foundation.

As the book project drew to a close I was able to call on several of Prof. Głomb's friends for assistance. Jan Plachta, a Professional Civil Engineer living in Chicago, was able to supply me with more photos, some guidance as to bridge dimensions and check some of my translation, while Prof. Zbigniew Bzymek made many detailed and valuable comments about it.

Ralph Modjeski Pattison, great-grandson of Ralph Modjeski, signs autographs on the Benjamin Franklin Bridge during ceremonies on July 1, 2001.

During this time I was also making efforts to gather additional illustrations by creating a collection of old postcards of Modjeski's bridges (several are featured in this book) and taking my own photographs of the Modjeski-built bridges in our area. I must admit that having spent most of my life in Philadelphia I had never been on the walkways of the Benjamin Franklin Bridge until the day that I decided to try a few photographs there. I had a wonderful afternoon looking at the city from an entirely novel perspective while feeling the gentle undulations of the pedestrian deck as traffic and trains rumbled on the level below. My experiences on the Tacony-Palmyra Bridge were less pleasant. The New Jersey State Police ordered me off the bridge, not for impeding traffic, but because of a regulation forbidding picture taking after September 11, 2001. This regulation is no doubt unconstitutional, but at the time I was not willing to put it to the test. What a contrast to Prof. Bzymek's experience in photography a few years ago on the Mackinac Bridge, located over the Mackinac Straits in Michigan. There the bridge police provided a police escort car, to prevent him from being accidentally struck by an inattentive motorist.

I took pictures of several other Modjeski and Masters bridges on the East Coast. Especially satisfying was finding the correct angle to photograph the massive railroad draw bridge at New London, Connecticut. And no one tried to chase me off when I photographed the stately arches of the Market Street Bridge in Harrisburg, PA. It was there that I found cobwebs had covered the bronze tablet that bears the names of the engineers and builders. I cleaned them off, and hope that this book will also act to bring Ralph Modjeski's name into deserved prominence again.

In a way one can say that steps have been made in this direction already on July 1, 2001, the seventy-fifth anniversary of the bridge. On that day, a Sunday, the Benjamin Franklin Bridge was closed to motor traffic and thousands of people walked the bridge. A noontime ceremony that featured speeches by local dignitaries also included Ralph

Modjeski Pattison, the great grandson of the bridge builder, who spoke about his great-grandfather's immigrant beginnings. He was inserted into the ceremonies at the last moment by Michael Blichasz, the president of the local Polish American Congress, when we learned that Ralph had scheduled a family trip to the area. At that time he shared with me some interesting materials that illustrate this book.

This project was not just the work of one person but a collaborative effort of many people who assisted as their resources allowed. I am most grateful to the sponsors who placed their ads in the book. These you may read on the pages that follow. But in addition to the persons already named I would like to thank Aleksandra Medvec for helping with the first draft translation, Monica Polowy Winter for proof reading the final version, and my parents Melania and Bonifacy Obst for their invaluable moral support as the press deadline approached.

Peter J. Obst
Philadelphia, Pennsylvania
July 1, 2002

Aleksandra Medvec inspects a segment of the Benjamin Franklin Bridge cable on display in front of the Franklin Institute in Philadelphia, PA.

THE WHITE HOUSE

July 23, 2002

Mr. Peter Obst
President
The Kosciuszko Foundation
Philadelphia Chapter
67 Lower Orchard Drive
Levittown, Pennsylvania 19056-2722

Dear Mr. Obst,

Meeting you at the Polish American Cultural Center was a pleasure, and I am delighted that you could attend the program.

Thank you for the book, *A Man Who Spanned Two Eras*. Translating this book into English must have been a challenging task and a labor of love. You should be pleased with the final product!

President Bush joins me in sending best wishes.

Sincerely,

Laura Bush

Sponsors

In Appreciation of His Legacy

The Ben Stefanski Family
of Cleveland, Ohio

Ben S. Stefanski II

B.S.I.E.

Christina Stefanski, B.S.I.E. Purdue '94

and

August Vetterino

Ben S. Stefanski III and Heather Stefanski, E.M.S
Princeton '95, M.B.A. and M.E.D. Stanford '99

and

Ben S. IV

Salutes

from the

Polish Cultural Institute...

...a recently established mission of the Polish Ministry of Foreign Affairs. Based in New York City, the Institute is dedicated to nurturing and promoting cultural ties between the United States and Poland, both through American exposure to Polish cultural achievement, and through exposure of Polish artists and scholars to American trends, institutions, and professional counterparts.

We take an active collaborative role in the promotion, organization, and in many cases the actual production of a broad range of cultural events in theater, music, film, literature, and the fine arts. With its extensive contacts in America and Poland, the Institute is in an excellent position to help such initiatives in a variety of ways that include fund-raising, facilitating contacts in Poland, organizing concurrent panels of artists and scholars, generating press coverage, and developing public outreach.

For more information, please visit our website at
www.PolishCulture-NYC.org
or write to **mail@polishculture-nyc.org**

or visit us at the

Polish Cultural Institute
Suite 4621
350 Fifth Avenue
New York, NY 10118

Helena Modrzejewska

(Helena Modjeska)

1840 – 1909

Rudolf Modrzejewski

(Ralph Modjeski)

1861 – 1940

Benjamin Franklin Bridge

built in 1926

It is not without pride that the Polish Cultural Institute salutes the 75th birthday of the Benjamin Franklin Bridge, as well as the book that celebrates it… about a man - and his mother -   whose lives, spanning two centuries, two continents, and two cultures, exemplified in the best possible sense what it meant to be new Americans from Poland.

POLISH-AMERICAN ENGINEERS ASSOCIATION HONORS RALPH MODJESKI

The Polish-American Engineers Association in Chicago was formed in 1934 by a group of engineers, scientists and architects. The objective of this organization is to advance and sustain the science of engineering. We continually strive to develop and expand the organization by attracting young engineers of Polish heritage. Our other objective is to propagate contributions of Polish-American engineers to the betterment of the United States and to foster closer relations among engineers and other professional people of related fields.

In 1991, on the 130th anniversary of Ralph Modjeski birth, the Polish American Engineers Association unveiled a memorial plaque at the Copernicus Center in Chicago.

Our Ralph Modjeski scholarship program presents every year two $500 scholarships to qualified engineering students of Polish descent.

Miroslaw Niedzinski, President
Jan Plachta, 1st Vice President
Walter Rymsza, 2nd Vice President
Andrzej Czyszczon, Treasurer
Jacek Zaworski, Secretary
Stanislaw Witczak, Financial Secretary

In 1931, 70-year-old Ralph Modjeski received the Washington Award. During the festivities a poem was read that beautifully summarizes his life accomplishments:

An old man, traveling a lone highway,
Came at this evening, cold and gray,
To a chasm vast and deep and wide.
The old man crossed in the twilight dim,
For the sullen stream held no fears for him,
But he turned when he reached the other side,
And builded a bridge to span the tide.

"Old man," cried a fellow pilgrim near,
"Your journey will end with the ending day,
And you never will pass this way,
You have crossed the chasm deep and wide,
Why build you this bridge at eventide?"

The builder raised his old gray head,
"Good friend, on the path I have come," he said,
"There followed after me today
A youth whose feet will pass this way
This stream, which has been as naught to me,
To that fair-haired boy may a pitfall be,
He, too, must cross in the twilight dim,
Good friend, I am building the bridge for him."

We remember and honor this great son of Poland

Jan S. Plachta, Ph.D., P.E., S.E.

PIASECKI AIRCRAFT

PIONEERS in VERTICAL LIFT

Since 1940

WORKING TO ADVANCE ROTORCRAFT TECHNOLOGY

Piasecki Aircraft Corporation (PiAC) is an Aerospace Engineering and Manufacturing Company with a focus on the development of Advanced Vertical Lift Aircraft. Mr. Frank N. Piasecki, President and Chairman of the Board, is one of the original pioneers of the helicopter industry, with the development of the second successful helicopter in the United States and the first successful tandem rotor transport helicopter in the world. PiAC was founded after Mr. Piasecki's departure from the original Piasecki Helicopter Corporation.

In all, the Piasecki Company is responsible for development of over 28 different vertical lift aircraft, the technology from which has resulted in generation of over $16 billion of direct economic activity for the U.S., including revenue from export to many countries. Piasecki assisted PZL Swidnik of Poland in FAA certification of their W-3A helicopter awarded in 1993. In 1986 President Ronald Reagan awarded Frank N. Piasecki National Medal of Technology in recognition of these achievements. The Piasecki Aircraft Corp. operates at a 100,000 sq.ft. engineering and manufacturing facility located in Essington, Pennsylvania.

PIASECKI AIRCRAFT CORPORATION

Second Street West
P.O. Box 360
Essington, PA 19029-0360

Phone: (610) 521-5700
Fax: (610) 521-5935
E-mail: info@piasecki.com

POLISH NATIONAL ALLIANCE
Largest Ethnic Fraternal Benefit Society
In The United States

Extends Congratulations To
The Philadelphia Chapter
of the
KOSCIUSZKO FOUNDATION
upon publication of the biography of
RALPH MODJESKI

Executive Committee:
Edward J. Moskal, President
Teresa N. Abick, Vice President
Stanley M. Jendzejec, Vice President
Frank J. Spula, Secretary
Casimir J. Musielak, Treasurer

Supervisory Council
Hilary S. Czaplicki, Censor
Z. John Ordon, Vice Censor

Headquarters:
6100 N. Cicero Avenue, Chicago, Illinois 60646-4385
Telephone: 773-286-0500 - Toll Free: 1-800-621-3723

Visit Our Website At
www.pna-znp.org

Ralph
Modjeski

bRidgebuilder

**NOT ONLY BRIDGES
BUT ALSO
Giorgio PIEROGIES
BRING PEOPLE TOGETHER**

ADAMBA IMPORTS

Adamba Imports is proudly offering gourmet foods and exquisite spirits under the following brand names:

H&H

www.Adamba.com
www.Luksusova.com
www.InkaCoffee.com
www.UltimatVodka.com
www.TearsofScotland.com
www.BisonGrassVodka.com

VAVEL®

DELAWARE RIVER

18666 wires

MANHATTAN

9472 wires

WILLIAMSBURG

7696 wires

BROOKLYN

5358 wires

Paul Philippe Cret, founder of H2L2 Architects/Planners and architect of the Benjamin Franklin Bridge, worked together with Ralph Modjeski to create not only a timeless piece of architectural history, but a work of art. Today the bridge still stands proudly, serving as a major artery between Philadelphia, Pennsylvania and Camden, New Jersey. Looking back on Cret's legacy of work, some might say that he had a knack for beautiful design. Others would say that he had it wired.

philadelphia.pa.www.H2L2.com

paul philippe cret 1962

H2L2

Polish Heritage Society
of Philadelphia

Remembering
Ralph Modjeski's Contributions

Polish Heritage Society Officers

President .... Marie Hejnosz
Vice President .... Debbie Majka
Treasurer... Eleanor McGinley
Corresponding Secretary .... Irene Musman
Recording Secretary .... George Szymanski

Polish Heritage Society Directors

Eleanor Lerke
Stella Matczak
Peter Obst
Frank Przybylski
Andrew Pustelniak
Lottie Wojeck

American Council
for
Polish Culture

Carol Ogrodnik

Robert Ogrodnik

Anna Chrypinski

Ted Mirecki
company matching grant

Jacqueline Kolowski

Gena Falkowska

Marion and Jo Louise Winters

Polish American Association of Harrisburg, Inc.

Bogumila "Bo" Mangam, president
Agata Czopek, vice president
Frank Oscilowski, treasurer
Thomas Duszak, secretary
Wojciech Wyczalkowski, board member
Bill Boshinski, board member
Norman Kee, board member
Nancy Coleman Miller, board member

PRIDE AND PERFORMANCE

GENERAL CONTRACTORS
516 HANLEY INDUSTRIAL CT. ST. LOUIS MO 63144
PHONE: 314-647-3535   FAX: 314-647-5302
KANDSCORP@AOL.COM

JOHN J. KRASKA
CHAIRMAN
(President of St. Louis, MO -
Szczecin Poland Sister Cities)

THOMAS J. KRASKA
PRESIDENT

POLISH WOMEN'S ALLIANCE OF AMERICA

A Fraternal Benefit Society Helping Families Since 1898

205 S. Northwest Highway
Park Ridge, IL 60068
Toll Free: 1-888-522-1898
www.pwaa.org

National Officers:
Virginia Sikora, President   Sharon Zago, Vice-President
Grazyna Migala, Secretary General   Olga Kaszewicz, Treasurer

National Directors:
Jennie Starzyk Benton, Marcia Mackiewicz Duffy, Carmen Czerwinski
Helen Simmons, Antoinette Trella Vander Noot

Advisory:
Dr. Wieczorek - Medical Examiner
Stone, Pogrund & Korey - Legal Counsel

"MOTHER OF ALL POLISH FRATERNALS"

Are you a member of the Polish Roman
Catholic Union? Why not join us...

CELEBRATING 129 YEARS OF SERVICE
1873 - 2002

EXECUTIVE BOARD

WALLACE M. OZOG, FICF, **PRESIDENT**
JERRY S. KUCHARSKI, FICF, **RESIDENT VICE PRESIDENT**
RICHARD MISIUDA, **FIRST VICE PRESIDENT**
JOSEPHINE SZAROWICZ, **SECRETARY-TREASURER**

NATIONAL HEADQUARTERS
984 N. Milwaukee Ave, Chicago, IL 60622
(773) 782-2600 or (800) 772-8632
fax (773) 278-4595   http://www.prcua.org

In Memory Of

Leonard V. Kosinski, Ph.D.
1923 - 1997
Scholar and Polish Activist

Awarded the Cavalier's Cross, Order of Merit, Republic of Poland
by Lech Walesa, President of Poland, May 5, 1994

Recipient of the Founder's Award of the
American Counsel for Polish Culture
August 17, 1996

Founder and President of the
Polish Heritage Association of the Southeast
Aiken, South Carolina (PHASE-A) 1985 - 1997

West Point alumnus - 82nd Airborne, WWII

"His life was gentle, and the elements
So mix'd in him that Nature might stand up
And say to all the world, "This was a Man!"
- Wm. Shakespeare

Spij Spokojnie - Rest in Peace, sweet prince

Officers & Members of the American Polish Engineering Association Detroit, Michigan

Bridging the Centuries

Polish Contributions to American Life

On the occasion of the **75th Anniversary** of the Benjamin Franklin Bridge, the Members of the Associated Polish Home remember and celebrate Ralph Modjeski, whose contribution years ago continues to benefit Americans today.

Stowarzyszenie Domu Polskiego wlacza sie do uczczenia 75-tej rocznicy istnienia mostu Benjamina Franklina zbudowanego przez naszego rodaka Rudolfa Modrzejewskiego!

The Associated Polish Home
of Philadelphia
9150 Academy Road
Philadelphia, PA, 19114-2885

American Institute of Polish Culture

9190 49th Street N.
Pinellas Park, FL 33782-5228

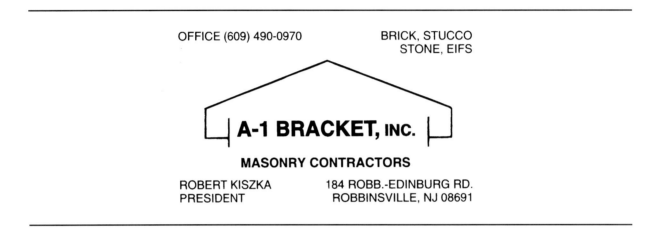

OFFICE (609) 490-0970   BRICK, STUCCO
STONE, EIFS

A-1 BRACKET, INC.

MASONRY CONTRACTORS

ROBERT KISZKA   184 ROBB.-EDINBURG RD.
PRESIDENT   ROBBINSVILLE, NJ 08691

We are proud to acknowledge the achievements of Polish-born engineer Ralph Modjeski

Dr. and Mrs. Alfred Halas

75th Anniversary Greetings

COLONEL FRANCIS C. KAJENCKI (RET)
Author of
Thaddeus Kosciuszko: Military Engineer of the American Revolution (1998)
and
Casimir Pulaski: Cavalry Commander of the American Revolution (2001)

Published by Southwest Polonia Press, El Paso Texas

George and Anne Szymanski
Philadelphia, Pennsylvania

American Council for Polish Culture

(ACPC)

CHESTER T. CYZIO
ATTORNEY AT LAW

PHONE (215) 568-6220   1429 WALNUT ST., 8TH FLOOR
FAX (215) 564-2859   PHILADELPHIA, PA 19102

Polonia Technica, Inc.

208 East 30th Street
New York, NY 10016

Irene Musman
Huntingdon Valley, Pennsylvania
•

Debbie and Henry Majka
Philadelphia, Pennsylvania
•

Congratulations!
Dr. and Mrs. Raymond A. Pietak

Two views of the Benjamin Franklin bridge showing the roadway (left) and the railway line that connects Philadelphia, PA with Camden, NJ.

•

Anonymous Donor
from Portland, Connecticut

•

Kulpicki Family
Stanley Z. Kulpicki, Helen M. Kulpicki, Stephen J. Kulpicki, P.E.

•

Mr. and Mrs. Carl F. Gregory

•

Commemorating the life of Rudolf Modrzejewski
and joining this celebration of Polish Pride …
Walter, Teresa, Terri, Marie, Wladzio, and Julia Wojcik

•

Pro Arte Associates Promotional Agency — Regina Gorzkowska
Museum Towers, Apt. 1513, 1801 Buttonwood Street, Phila., PA 19143
tel: (215) 563-6669   e-mail:proartrg@icpc.com

•

We honor our Parents and Sister,
Stanley and Cecelia Pretkiewicz Kuklinski, Marianne Kuklinski
from Stephen, Louise, Charles, Peter, Vincent Kuklinski and Families

•

With Best Wishes from the Tyszka Family
Mary Ellen, Fred and Annette, Henry J., Beth and Munther,
AJ Louni, Anne and Paul Dyhdalo
(Ruth, Vince, Ben, Victoria, Adam, Alek, Jordan, Steven and Lydia)

•

Malgorzata Siekierska Romanski, MD
Philadelphia, Pennsylvania

•

Dr. Janusz Romanski
Piasecki Aircraft Corporation
Essington, Pennsylvania

•

S. Paul Bosse
Yardley, Pennsylvania

•

Philadelphia Chapter of the Kosciuszko Foundation

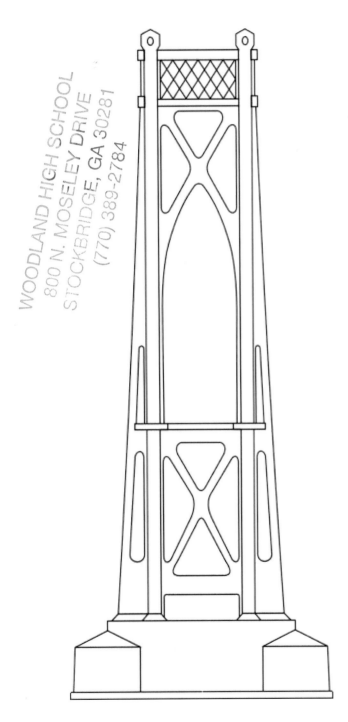

Tower of the Mid-Hudson (Roosevelt)
Bridge in Poughkeepsie, New York
drawing by Gabriela Paciorek

WOODLAND HIGH SCHOOL
800 N. MOSELEY DRIVE
STOCKBRIDGE, GA 30281
(770) 389-2784

A Man Who Spanned Two Eras

Ralph Modjeski (Rudolph Modrzejewski 1861 – 1940), son of actress Helena Modrzejewska, was one of America's great bridge builders. Educated at the famous École des Ponts et Chaussées in Paris, he interned with George Morison, one of America's pioneering bridge engineers. Later, he started the firm of Modjeski and Masters going on to build some of the great bridges in the United States.

In the Philadelphia area he built the Benjamin Franklin Bridge, the Tacony-Palmyra Bridge, and two bridges on Henry Avenue. His other major projects included the Thebes Bridge at Thebes, Illinois; the San Francisco-Oakland Bay Bridge, and the Huey P. Long Bridge in New Orleans. During a long career he introduced many advances in the design of long steel truss and suspension bridges, and was one of the first engineers in the United States to build large structures of reinforced concrete.

He received many awards for his work including the Franklin Institute Franklin Medal (1922), the John Fritz Medal (1930) and the Washington Award (1931) given for his "contribution to transportation through superior skill and courage in bridge construction and design." The firm he founded continues to design and build bridges, maintaining the legacy he established.

• **You can order a copy** of "A Man Who Spanned Two Eras" (over 70 b/w illustrations, color soft cover) by sending $18.95 (plus $4.50 shipping) to:

Kosciuszko Foundation, Philadelphia Chapter, c/o Maria Strek-Dziedzic, 109 Nicolson Drive, Downingtown PA 19335. Checks can be made out to "KF Philadelphia."

Ask about multiple copy discounts. More information can be found on the web page:
www.polishcultureacpc.org/Modjeski.html